PERFECT BALANCE

Inquiry through
science, math and
technology

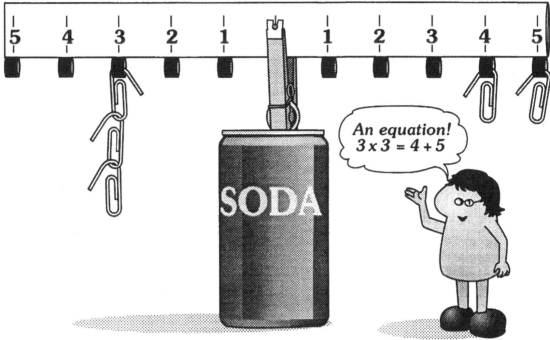

SCIENCE WITH SIMPLE THINGS SERIES

Conceived and
written by
RON MARSON

Illustrated by
PEG MARSON

LEARNING SYSTEMS

342 S Plumas Street
Willows, CA 95988

www.topscience.org

WHAT CAN YOU COPY?

Dear Educator,

Please honor our copyright restrictions. We offer liberal options and guidelines below with the intention of balancing your needs with ours. When you buy these labs and use them for your own teaching, you sustain our work. If you "loan" or circulate copies to others without compensating TOPS, you squeeze us financially, and make it harder for our small non-profit to survive. Our well-being rests in your hands. Please help us keep our low-cost, creative lessons available to students everywhere. Thank you!

PURCHASE, ROYALTY and LICENSE OPTIONS

TEACHERS, HOMESCHOOLERS, LIBRARIES:

We do all we can to keep our prices low. Like any business, we have ongoing expenses to meet. We trust our users to observe the terms of our copyright restrictions. While we prefer that all users purchase their own TOPS labs, we accept that real-life situations sometimes call for flexibility.

Reselling, trading, or loaning our materials is prohibited unless one or both parties contribute an Honor System Royalty as fair compensation for value received. We suggest the following amounts – let your conscience be your guide.

HONOR SYSTEM ROYALTIES: If making copies from a library, or sharing copies with colleagues, please calculate their value at 50 cents per lesson, or 25 cents for homeschoolers. This contribution may be made at our website or by mail (addresses at the bottom of this page). Any additional tax-deductible contributions to make our ongoing work possible will be accepted gratefully and used well.

Please follow through promptly on your good intentions. Stay legal, and do the right thing.

SCHOOLS, DISTRICTS, and HOMESCHOOL CO-OPS:

PURCHASE Option: Order a book in quantities equal to the number of target classrooms or homes, and receive quantity discounts. If you order 5 books or downloads, for example, then you have unrestricted use of this curriculum for any 5 classrooms or families per year for the life of your institution or co-op.

2-9 copies of any title: 90% of current catalog price + shipping.

10+ copies of any title: 80% of current catalog price + shipping.

ROYALTY/LICENSE Option: Purchase just one book or download *plus* photocopy or printing rights for a designated number of classrooms or families. If you pay for 5 additional Licenses, for example, then you have purchased reproduction rights for an entire book or download edition for any **6** classrooms or families per year for the life of your institution or co-op.

1-9 Licenses: 70% of current catalog price per designated classroom or home.

10+ Licenses: 60% of current catalog price per designated classroom or home.

WORKSHOPS and TEACHER TRAINING PROGRAMS:

We are grateful to all of you who spread the word about TOPS. Please limit copies to only those lessons you will be using, and collect all copyrighted materials afterward. No take-home copies, please. Copies of copies are strictly prohibited.

Copyright © 2004 by TOPS Learning Systems. All rights reserved. This material is created/printed/transmitted in the United States of America. No part of this program may be used, reproduced, or transmitted in any manner whatsoever without written permission from the publisher, ***except as explicitly stated above and below***:

The ***original owner*** of this book or digital download is permitted to make multiple copies of all ***student materials*** for personal teaching use, provided all reproductions bear copyright notice. A purchasing school or homeschool co-op may assign ***one*** purchased book or digital download to ***one*** teacher, classroom, family, or study group ***per year***. Reproduction of student materials from libraries is permitted if the user compensates TOPS as outlined above. Reproduction of any copyrighted materials for commercial sale is prohibited.

For licensing, honor system royalty payments, contact: **www.TOPScience.org**; or **TOPS Learning Systems 342 S Plumas St, Willows CA 95988**; or inquire at **customerservice@topscience.org**

ISBN 978 - 0 - 941008 - 69 - 3

CONTENTS

PART I — PREPARATION AND SUPPORT

PART II — ACTIVITIES AND LESSON NOTES

PART III — SUPPLEMENTARY CUTOUTS

A TOPS Teaching Model

If science were only a set of explanations and a collection of facts, you could teach it with blackboard and chalk. You could require students to read chapters in a textbook, assign questions at the end of each chapter, and set periodic written exams to determine what they remember. Science is traditionally taught in this manner. Everybody studies the same information at the same time. Class togetherness is preserved.

But science is more than this. It is also process — a dynamic interaction of rational inquiry and creative play. Scientists probe, poke, handle, observe, question, think up theories, test ideas, jump to conclusions, make mistakes, revise, synthesize, communicate, disagree and discover. Students can understand science as process only if they are free to think and act like scientists, in a classroom that recognizes and honors individual differences.

Science is both a traditional body of knowledge and an individualized process of creative inquiry. Science as process cannot ignore tradition. We stand on the shoulders of those who have gone before. If each generation reinvents the wheel, there is no time to discover the stars. Nor can traditional science continue to evolve and redefine itself without process. Science without this cutting a static, dead thing.

ng model that combines both the content and process of science into an integrated whole. This model, like any scientific theory, must give way over time to new and better ideas. We challenge you to incorporate this TOPS model into your own teaching practice. Change it and make it better so it works for you.

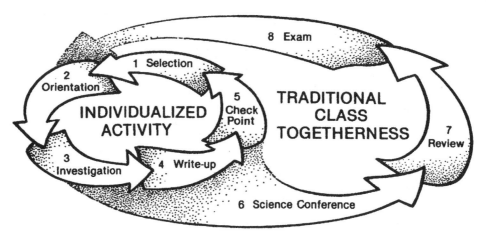

1. SELECTION

Students generally select activity pages in sequence, because new concepts build on old ones in a specific order. There are, however, exceptions to this pattern: students might skip a lesson that is not challenging; repeat an activity with doubtful results; add an experiment to answer their own "what-would-happen-if?" questions.

Working at their own pace, students fall into a natural routine that creates stability and order. They still have questions and problems, to be sure, but remain purposefully engaged with a definite sense of direction.

2. ORIENTATION

Any student with basic reading skills can successfully interpret our carefully designed activity page directions. If your class is new to TOPS, it may take a while for your students to get used to following directions by themselves, and to trust in their own problem-solving ability.

When students ask you for help, first ask them to read what they don't understand. If they didn't read the instruction in the first place, this should clear things up. Identify poor readers in your class. Whey they ask, "What does this mean?" they may be asking in reality, "Will you please read these directions aloud?"

Beyond reading comprehension, certain basic concepts and skills may also be necessary complete some activity sheets. You can't, for example, expect students to measure the length of something unless they know how to use a ruler as well. Anticipate and teach prerequisite concepts and skills (if any) at the beginning of each class period, before students begin their daily individualized work. Different age groups will require different levels of assistance: primary students will need more introductory support than middle school students; secondary students may require none at all.

A

3. INVESTIGATION

Students work through the activity pages independently and cooperatively, They follow their own experimental strategies and help each other. Encourage this behavior by helping students only after they have tried to help themselves. As a resource teacher, you work to stay out of the center of attention, responding to student questions rather than posing teacher questions.

Some students will progress more rapidly than others. To finish as a cohesive group, announce well in advance when individualized study will end. Expect to generate a frenzy of activity as students rush to meet your deadline. While slower students finish those core activities you specify, challenge your more advanced students with Extension activities, or to design original experiments.

4. WRITE-UP

Activity pages ask students to explain the how and why of things. Answers may be brief and to the point, with the exception of those that require creative writing. Students may accelerate their pace by completing these reports out of class.

Students may work alone, or in cooperative lab groups. But each one should prepare an original write-up, and bring it to you for approval. Avoid an avalanche of write-ups near the end of the unit by enforcing this simple rule: each write-up must be approved before starting the next activity.

5. CHECK POINT

Student and teacher together evaluate each write-up on a pass/no-pass basis. Thus no time is wasted haggling over grades. If reasonable effort has been demonstrated consistent with ability, check off or initial the corresponding activity number that students have listed in their notebooks or assignment folders kept on file in class.

Because each student is present when you evaluate, feedback is immediate and effective. A few moments of your personal attention is surely more effective than tedious margin notes that students may not heed or understand. Remember, you don't have to point out every error. Zero in on particular weaknesses. If reasonable effort is not evident, direct students to make specific improvements and return for a final check.

A responsible lab assistant can double the amount of individual attention each student receives. If he or she is mature and respected by your students, have the assistant check even-numbered write-ups, while you check the odd ones. This will balance the work load and assure equal treatment.

6. SCIENCE CONFERENCE

Individualized study has ended. This is a time for students to come together, to discuss experimental results, to debate and draw conclusions. Slower students learn about the enrichment activities of faster classmates. Those who did original investigations or made unusual discoveries share this information with their peers, just like scientists at a real conference.

This conference is an opportunity to expand ideas, explore relevancy and integrate subject areas. Consider bringing in films, newspaper articles and community speakers. It's a meaningful time to investigate the technological and social implications of the topic you are studying. Make it an event to remember.

7. REVIEW

Does your school have an adopted science textbook? Do parts of your science syllabus still need to be covered? Now is the time to integrate traditional science resources into your overall program. Your students already share a common background of hands-on lab work. With this base of experience, they can now read the text with greater understanding, think and problem-solve more successfully, communicate more effectively.

You might spend just a day here, or an entire week. Finish with a review of major concepts in preparation for the final exam. Our review/test questions provide an excellent resource for discussion and study.

8. EXAM

Use any combination of our review/test questions, plus questions of your own, to determine how well students have mastered the concepts they've been learning.

Now that your class has completed a major TOPS learning cycle, it's time to start fresh with a brand new topic. Those who messed up and got behind don't need to stay there. Everyone begins the new topic on an equal footing. This frequent change of pace encourages your students to work hard, to enjoy what they learn, and thereby grow in scientific literacy.

B

Getting Ready

Here is a checklist of things to think about and preparations to make before beginning your first lesson on PERFECT BALANCE.

✔ Review the scope and sequence.

Take just a few minutes now to page through all 20 lessons. Pause to read each *Objective* (top left column of the Teaching Notes) and scan each lesson.

✔ Budget your class time.

Allow an average of 1 class period per lesson (more for younger students), plus time for discussion, review and testing. If you teach science every day, this book will happily engage your students for about 4 weeks. If your schedule doesn't allow this much TOPS, consult the logic tree on page E to see which activities best fit your syllabus, and what you can skip without breaking conceptual links. Even if you can afford to budget only a few hours, you'll see how to do it on page E.

✔ Review grade level options:

middle grades 4-9

Average readers in this grade span can successfully use these TOPS materials as designed, and grow into independent learners. Encourage students to read the directions and figure things out for themselves. They will grow in confidence, academic ability and scientific literacy.

lower primary K-3

Adapt these materials to reach *down* as follows:

MATH BALANCE sequence

You build the Math Balance yourself (activities 1-2) and set up an "Inquiry Corner" in your classroom.

a. Free play: Provide a bowl with several dozen paper clips ("arms" bent slightly open).

b. Directed play: As above, but students use activity 3, perhaps multiple times, to record their findings.

c. Puzzles: Add activities 4-9 as children are able.

WEIGHING sequence

You build the Paper Beam Balance yourself (activities 11-12). Establish a second "Inquiry Corner" in your classroom, *or* reorganize the first one.

a. Free play: Provide an egg carton with objects to compare and weigh in its twelve cups: two with paper clips as above; one with tenths of paper clips (activity 15); one with pinto beans and one with popcorn, each selected for fairly uniform size; a cup with lentils; one with a pre-1982 penny and a shiny post-1982 penny; one with matched bottle caps; a cup with styrofoam packing peanuts; a clothespin; and a few other coins (unless theft is an issue); and finally, sugar cubes (unless eating is an issue). Please substitute other items of your own choice, of course. A package of variety bean soup mix offers additional seed choices, if you select for uniform size.

b. Directed play: Continue activity with egg carton materials as above. Students ask themselves questions, do experiments, report findings, and write equations on notebook paper.

c. Puzzles: Add activities, 19 and 18 as children are able.

high school 10-12

Adapt these materials to reach *up* as follows:

MATH BALANCE sequence

a. Students independently build balances (activities 1-2).

b. Photocopy and staple class sets of activities 3-10. Have students investigate the properties of their Math Balances over a limited time frame (perhaps 1 or 2 class periods.) Ask older, more capable students to report their findings on notebook paper, leaving the activities unmarked.

c. Arrange for your most capable students to take their balances and unmarked activity sheets into a lower grade and teach other children.

WEIGHING sequence

a. Students independently build an equal-arm balance (activities 11-12).

b. Photocopy and staple class sets of activities 14, 15, 18, 19. Ask students to do experiments of interest in preparation for cross-age teaching, as above, reporting results on their own notebook paper.

c. Assign these activity clusters as independent investigations. From easiest to most challenging they are: 13, 16-17, 20 and 15 (with extensions).

✔ Collect needed materials.

See page D, opposite, for details.

✔ Organize a way to track assignments.

A box with a brick makes a fine file cabinet for collecting student work. File folders or notebooks make suitable organizers. Students will feel a sense of accomplishment as their completed assignments build into impressive portfolios. Since all papers stay together, reference and review are facilitated.

Ask students to tape a numbered sheet of paper in the front cover of their folders or notebooks. Track individual progress by initialing lesson numbers as daily assignments pass your check point.

✔ Communicate your grading expectations.

Your students need to understand how they will be assessed. We encourage a scheme that counts individual effort, attitude and overall achievement. We think these three components deserve equal weight.

Gathering Materials

Listed below is everything you'll need to teach this module. Buy what you don't already have from your local supermarket, drugstore or hardware store. Ask students to bring recycled materials from home.

Keep this classification key in mind as you review what's needed.

general on-the-shelf materials:	special in-a-box materials:
Normal type suggests that these materials are used often. Keep these basics on shelves or in drawers that are readily accessible to your students. The next TOPS module you teach will likely utilize many of these same materials.	Italic type suggests that these materials are un- usual. Keep these specialty items in a separate box. After you finish teaching this module, label the box for storage and put it away, ready to use again.
(substituted materials):	*optional materials:
Parentheses enclosing any item suggests a ready substitute. These alternatives may work just as well as the original. Don't be afraid to improvise, to make do with what you have.	An asterisk sets these items apart. They are nice to have, but you can easily live without them. They are probably not worth an extra trip to the store, unless you are gathering other materials as well.

Everything is listed in order of first use. Start gathering at the top of this list and work down. Ask students to bring recycled items from home. The Teaching Notes may occasionally suggest additional *Extensions*. Materials for these optional experiments are listed neither here nor under *Materials*. Read the extension itself to determine what new items, if any, are required.

Quantities depend on how many students you have, how you organize them into activity groups, and how you teach. Decide which of these 3 estimates best applies to you, then adjust quantities up or down as necessary:

$Q_1/Q_2/Q_3$

Single Student: Enough for 1 student to do all the experiments.
Individualized Approach: Enough for 30 students informally working in pairs, all self-paced.
Traditional Approach: Enough for 30 students, organized into pairs, all doing the same lesson.

KEY:	*special in-a-box materials* (substituted materials)	general on-the-shelf materials *optional materials

$Q_1/Q_2/Q_3$

1/15/15	scissors
1 roll	clear tape
1 roll	masking tape
1/15/15	spring-action clothespins
various	("pincushion" material: small styrofoam cups, foam "packing peanuts," corrugated cardboard, corks or clothespins – see teaching notes 10)
1 pkg	straight pins, 1 inch or 2.5 cm – choose steel pins if you plan to teach TOPS magnetism units
1/15/15	pop-top soda cans with attached finger tabs (small beverage bottles) – see teaching notes 2, step 3
3/30/30	paper clips, boxes of 100, standard size - only 3 boxes needed if you do Activity 20 as a teacher demonstration – we used Acco #1 paper clips – see teaching note 13
1/15/15	cups sand (gravel, beans, or other ballast material) – see teaching notes 2, step 7
1/1/1	lump modeling clay
1/4/15	index cards, standard 3 x 5 inch
10/40/150	thumbtacks (pushpins) that are heavier than your paper clips
1 pgk each	popcorn, lentils, long-grained rice
1/10/15	calculators
1/4/15	objects to weigh: post-1982 pennies, nickels, notebook paper
various	(other objects to weigh – see teaching notes 14, step 2)
1 bag	pinto beans
1/1/1	bowl (margarine tub or equivalent)

Sequencing Activities

This logic tree shows how all 20 activities tie together. In general, students begin at the tree trunk and work up through the related branches. Lower level activities support higher ones. Leaves that open vertically into higher leaves form logical pairs that belong together. Horizontal activities cover similar concepts that you can teach or skip.

Perfect Balance covers a broad range of content areas. Select those topics below that fit your syllabus, then use this logic tree to create your own scope and sequence. Parentheses in the upper right corner of each activity page are blank so you can pencil in the number sequence best tailored to your clasroom needs.

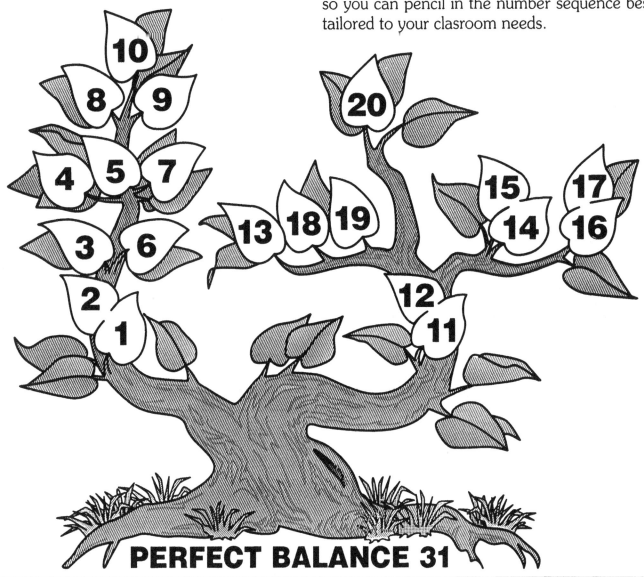

PERFECT BALANCE 31

SCIENCE

Inquiry/Process Skills: 1-20

Machines (Levers): 3-10

Standards of Weight
    paper clips: 14, 15
    paper squares: 16, extension 16
    grams: extension 15

Mass and Density: extensions 14 and 15

Metrics: extension 15

MATH

Equalities and Inequalities: 3-10

Dependent Variables
    weight and area: 18
    weight and number: 19

Unit Analysis: 13, 16

Graphing
    linear: extensions 16 and 19
    bar graph distribution: 17
    asymptotic: 20

Statistics: 17

TECHNOLOGY

Scratch Construction
    analog computer: 1, 2
    equal-arm balance: 10, 11

Inventions: extension 16B

Gaining a Whole Perspective

Science is more than facts, more than theories. It is a fascinating and complex fabric of experience, observation, and discovery. Weave in enrichment activities offered as extensions throughout this book. Follow strands of connection with the open-ended ideas below. Do science!

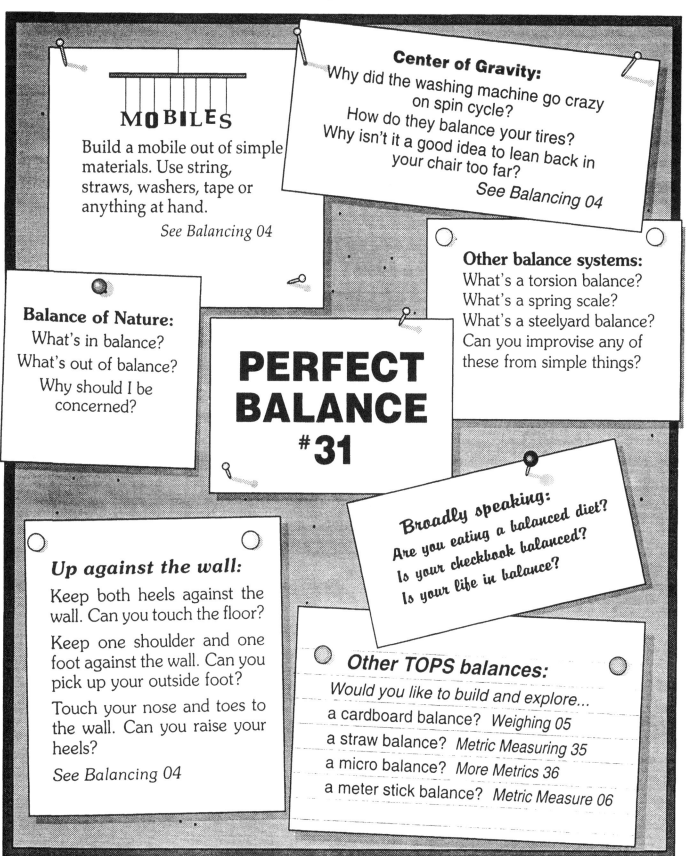

MOBILES

Build a mobile out of simple materials. Use string, straws, washers, tape or anything at hand.

See Balancing 04

Center of Gravity:

Why did the washing machine go crazy on spin cycle?
How do they balance your tires?
Why isn't it a good idea to lean back in your chair too far?

See Balancing 04

Balance of Nature:

What's in balance?
What's out of balance?
Why should I be concerned?

PERFECT BALANCE #31

Other balance systems:

What's a torsion balance?
What's a spring scale?
What's a steelyard balance?
Can you improvise any of these from simple things?

Up against the wall:

Keep both heels against the wall. Can you touch the floor?

Keep one shoulder and one foot against the wall. Can you pick up your outside foot?

Touch your nose and toes to the wall. Can you raise your heels?

See Balancing 04

Broadly speaking:

Are you eating a balanced diet?
Is your checkbook balanced?
Is your life in balance?

Other TOPS balances:

Would you like to build and explore...
a cardboard balance? *Weighing 05*
a straw balance? *Metric Measuring 35*
a micro balance? *More Metrics 36*
a meter stick balance? *Metric Measure 06*

Review / Test Questions

Photocopy these test questions. Cut out those you wish to use, and tape them onto white paper. Include questions of your own design, as well. Crowd them all onto a single page for students to answer on their own papers, or leave space for student responses after each question, as you wish. Duplicate a class set, and your custom-made test is ready to use. Use leftover questions as a class review in preparation for a final exam.

activity 1-2

When following directions, which of the following statements can you say is true? Circle one or more.

a. It is important to read carefully.

b. Pictures can help me understand.

c. I should wait for my teacher to explain everything.

activity 2

Before I use my balance, I should center it. I can do this by adding a little tape to the _____ arm.

activity 3

Use your math balance (if necessary) to decide if this beam balances:

activity 4

Draw two more x's to make this beam balance. Choose your positions so you can write a *different* equation in each box.

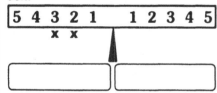

activity 5

Draw x's only under positions 3 and 4 to make this beam balance. Write a multiplication equation in each box.

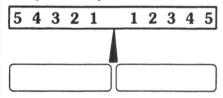

activity 6

Draw 4 different ways to make this beam balance by adding **3** paper clips to the right arm:

ADD THREE CLIPS

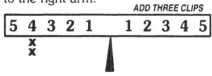

activity 7

Write an equation in each box. Does this beam balance?

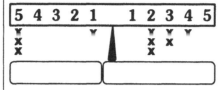

activity 8

Which of these beams balance? Show your math.

A.

B.

C.

activity 9

Find the beam that tilts **left**. Show your math.

A.

B.

C.

activity 10

Number the tab positions correctly. Then write an equation in each box to show that this unequal-arm beam balances.

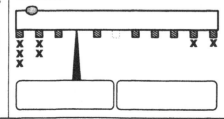

activity 13

If ten pennies weigh 62 paper clips, and 10 paper clips weigh 150 staples, how many staples does a penny weigh? Show your units.

activity 14

Teacher prep: Make paper weights of random sizes. Weigh them in paper clips; trim smaller or add tape until equal to an even number of clips. Fold and label them A, B, C....

Weigh 3 different prepared weights to the nearest whole paper clip on your paper beam balance. Label your answers by letter.

activity 15

Teacher prep: Add tape or cut away paper on the weights above. (Reserve a few originals for make-up tests). Circle the letter labels on the altered weights.

Weigh 3 different prepared weights to the nearest tenth of a paper clip on your balance. Label your answers by letter, and circle the letters.

activity 16

Find the weight of a nickel in paper squares. Use only 28 squares and clay.

activity 17

Find the **mode**, the **median**, and the **mean** for this data:

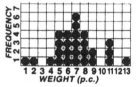

activity 18

Write an equation between A and B. Plug in areas to show it's true.

activity 19

How might you find out how much money is in a piggy bank full of dimes without breaking it open?

activity 20

Weights A and B hang from identical beams. Which weight is heavier? How do you know?

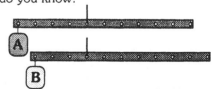

Copyright © 2004 by TOPS Learning Systems.

Answers

activity 1-2

a. true   **b**. true   **c**. false

activity 2

...add tape to the **_higher_** arm.

activity 3

The beam doesn't balance: the right side is heavier. *(5 is less than 2x3.)*

activity 4

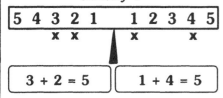

$$3 + 2 = 5 \qquad 1 + 4 = 5$$

activity 5

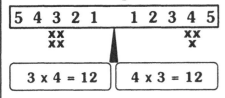

$$3 \times 4 = 12 \qquad 4 \times 3 = 12$$

activity 6

ADD THREE CLIPS

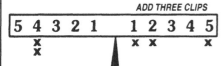

activity 7

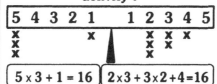

$$5 \times 3 + 1 = 16 \qquad 2 \times 3 + 3 \times 2 + 4 = 16$$

Yes, this beam balances.

activity 8

LEFT SIDE   /   RIGHT SIDE

A. $5 + 3 + 1 = 9$ / $\overset{(4)}{2 \times 2} + \overset{(8)}{4 \times 2} = 12$

This beam does not balance.

B. $\overset{(6)}{5 + 2 \times 3} + 1 = 12$ / $\overset{(6)}{2 + 3 \times 2} + 4 = 12$

This beam balances.

C. $\overset{(8)}{4 \times 2} + \overset{(6)}{2 \times 3} = 14$ / $\overset{(6)}{2 \times 3} + \overset{(6)}{3 \times 2} + 4 = 16$

This beam does not balance.

activity 9

LEFT SIDE   /   RIGHT SIDE

A. $5 + 4 + 3 + \overset{(4)}{2 \times 2} + \overset{(2)}{1 \times 2} = 18$ / $\overset{(8)}{4 \times 2} + \overset{(10)}{5 \times 2} = 18$

This beam balances.

B. $\overset{}{4 \times 2} + 2 \times 2 + 1 \times 2 = 14$ / $1 \times 2 + 2 + 3 + 4 \times 2 = 15$

This beam tilts right.

C. $\overset{(12)}{4 \times 3} + \overset{(6)}{2 \times 3} = 18$ / $\overset{(6)}{2 \times 3} + \overset{(6)}{3 \times 2} + 4 = 16$

This beam tilts left.

activity 10

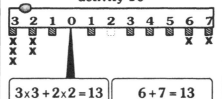

$$3 \times 3 + 2 \times 2 = 13 \qquad 6 + 7 = 13$$

activity 13

1 penny = 6.2 p.c.
1 p.c. = 15 staples

$$1 \text{ penny} = \frac{6.2 \ \cancel{p.c.}}{\text{penny}} \times \frac{15 \text{ staples}}{\cancel{p.c.}}$$

$$= 93 \text{ staples / penny}$$

activity 14

Student answers should be labeled with letters, and weights should be given in whole paper clips.
(Teacher should weigh and record an answer key.)

activity 15

*Student answers should be labeled with **circled** letters, and weights should be given to the nearest tenth of a paper clips.*
(Teacher should weigh and record an answer key.)

activity 16

Answers will vary with weight of paper used. We found...

1 nickel = 103 paper squares

activity 17

Mode: 7 p.c.
Median: 7 p.c.
Mean: 7 p.c.

activity 18

2 B = 5 A
rectangle B = 45 sq units
rectangle A = 18 sq units
2 x 18 = 2 x 45
90 = 90

activity 19

You might find out the value of the dimes by counterbalancing an identical empty piggy bank and a known number of dimes.

activity 20

Weight B is heavier because it supports the weight of the beam from a position closer to the pivot.

Copyright © 2004 by TOPS Learning Systems.

Why Teach TOPS?

Because your students have three brains – and multiple learning styles...

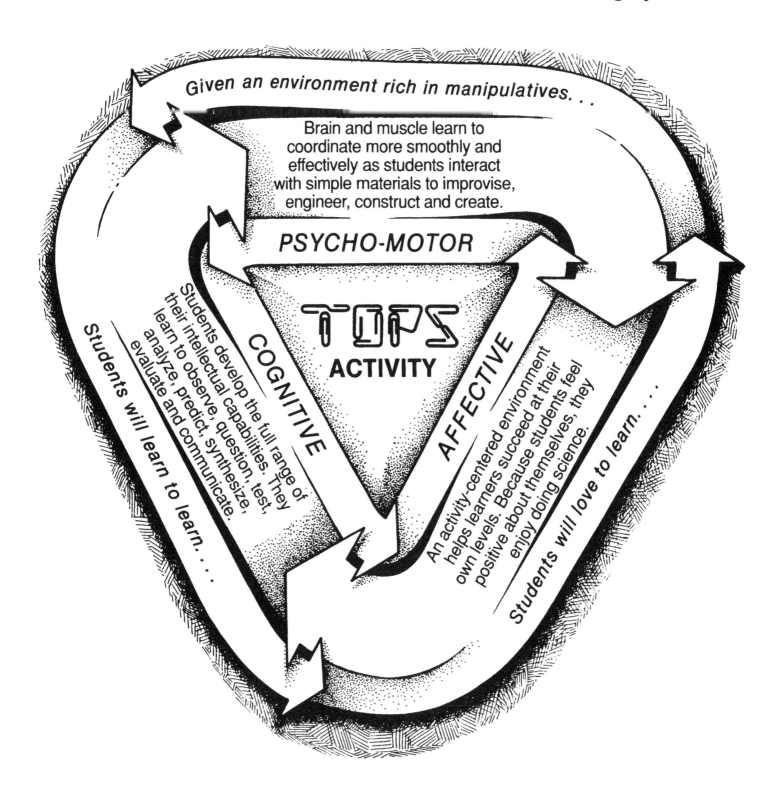

Given an environment rich in manipulatives. . .

Brain and muscle learn to coordinate more smoothly and effectively as students interact with simple materials to improvise, engineer, construct and create.

PSYCHO-MOTOR

TOPS ACTIVITY

COGNITIVE

Students develop the full range of their intellectual capabilities. They learn to observe, question, test, analyze, predict, synthesize, evaluate and communicate.

AFFECTIVE

An activity-centered environment helps learners succeed at their own levels. Because students feel positive about themselves, they enjoy doing science.

Students will learn to learn. . . .

Students will love to learn. . . .

ACTIVITIES
AND
LESSON NOTES
1-20

☞ As you duplicate and distribute these activity pages, **please observe our copyright restrictions** at the front of this book. Our basic rule is: **One book, one teacher.**

☞ TOPS is a small, not-for-profit educational corporation, dedicated to making great science accessible to students everywhere. Our survival depends on the sale of these inexpensive modules. If you would like to help spread the word that TOPS is tops, please request multiple copies of our **free TOPS Ideas catalog** to pass on to other educators or student teachers. These offer a variety of sample lessons, plus an order form for your colleagues to purchase their own TOPS modules. Thanks!

BUILD A MATH BALANCE (1)

1 **START HERE:**
Carefully trim this paper along the outside dashed line.

2 Fold it in half *exactly* along the center line. →

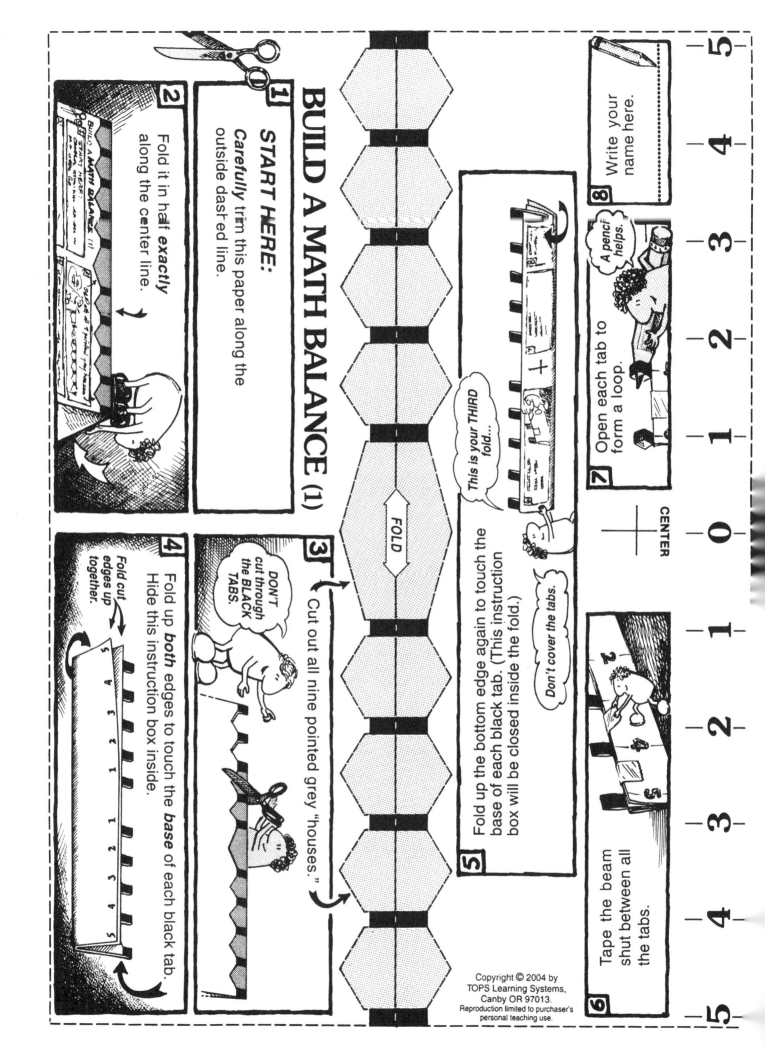

3 Cut out all nine pointed grey "houses." ↩

DON'T cut through the BLACK TABS.

4 Fold up *both* edges to touch the *base* of each black tab. Hide this instruction box inside.

Fold cut edges up together. ↗

FOLD

5 Fold up the bottom edge again to touch the base of each black tab. (This instruction box will be closed inside the fold.)

This is your THIRD fold...

Don't cover the tabs.

6 Tape the beam shut between all the tabs.

7 Open each tab to form a loop.

A pencil helps.

8 Write your name here.

CENTER

5 4 3 2 1 0 1 2 3 4 5

Copyright © 2004 by
TOPS Learning Systems,
Canby OR 97013.
Reproduction limited to purchaser's
personal teaching use.

Objective

To fold a paper beam that will be used in a math balance. To read and follow directions carefully.

Introduction/Orientation

In this activity and the next, students will build their own math balances. Before they start, build one yourself to familiarize yourself with the directions, and provide a model for your students to follow. In a homeschool situation where only one balance is needed, you might simply work closely with the child in assembling the two different balances in this book.

Many children have little experience following directions independently, and will seem puzzled or disengaged when presented with hands-on learning for the first time. Often poor reading skills or language difficulties are the cause. If you have students who are obviously not connecting with the worksheets, it may be helpful to work through the instructions with them as a group, perhaps building a model as an example. Read each step and make sure it's clear to all the children, perhaps asking volunteers to rephrase the needed actions in their own words. Savor the process of discovery and success along with them. Smile and shrug off small errors ("Hmm! That's science!"), and help them brainstorm ways to solve problems.

Don't rush this assembly process. Learning to read, interpret, and follow instructions is essential to children being engaged and successful in the enterprise of education, and is every bit as valuable as the other skills they will learn in lessons to follow. Gradually turn over the process of reading, interpreting, and doing to your students as they gain confidence. This can be a wonderfully satisfying process for kids (and for their teachers).

Though students who read at a third grade level or higher should be able to follow most instructions independently, these activities attract younger children, too. Pre-build beams for K-3 kids. Demonstrate how to hang the clips, balance the beam in a couple of simple examples, and then just let them play. Their own explorations will help them gain a kinesthetic "feel" for counting, quantifying, and math operations: this is the body intelligence that is the true value of child's play. Don't push them to the point where they become bored or begin to experience failure with this learning system. They can revisit these activities repeatedly in later years as their abstract thinking abilities grow stronger.

Lesson Notes

1. This worksheet folds into an actual balance beam as students complete the instructions 1-8 printed on it. If they follow the directions sequentially, students will experience few difficulties.

2. When folded carefully **on** the guide line, the edges of the paper won't quite meet. These edges will "creep" together as the beam is folded again in steps 4 and 5.

Folds should be well-defined, but knife-edge creases are not needed. In fact, the finished beams will be somewhat more rigid if the paper isn't creased sharply.

If students fold this instruction to the inside, ask them how they will read the next step. Higher steps always remain outside and visible for future direction.

3. Cutting out the grey "houses" leaves the beam with a row of black tabs. Students will achieve the neatest results by beginning two cuts *from the fold* for each house, ending at the peak of the "roof." (Continuous cuts from one side of the house to the other are more difficult, and are likely to produce uneven tabs, or result in cutting or tearing off tabs.)

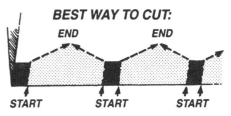

BEST WAY TO CUT:

If a tab is cut too narrow or sliced off altogether, students can reattach the fragment with clear tape. It might be easiest to unfold the page first, match and tape the paper bits, then fold again and recut.

4. **Both** bottom edges fold up to the base of the tabs. Students have a strong tendency to fold up only one edge, contrary to instructions. The tabs shouldn't be covered.

5. This is the third and final doubling. Watch for students who skip this step, resulting in a beam twice as deep (and half as strong) as it should be.

6. Snippets of tape should be roughly even, but in the next activity, students will adjust for inevitable weight differences in the two arms. Taping at three points will hold the paper in a beam, but taping between all tabs will make the balance easier to use.

7. Kids can often open the tabs into loops simply by pushing their folded edges up toward the beam. If this doesn't pop them open, though, a pencil point will help.

8. A completed beam should look like this.

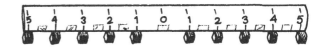

Your students' beams may not appear so well put together, but don't despair. Bad cuts and crooked folds notwithstanding, most beams still work quite well.

Evaluation

Do edges of the folded paper match more or less evenly? Are tabs well cut and pushed open to make loops? Is white paper trimmed away from the sides of the black tabs?

Materials

☐ A photocopy of the Math Balance (opposite page).
☐ Scissors.
☐ Transparent tape.

BUILD A MATH BALANCE (2)

1 Fold masking tape over the ends of a clothespin. Pinch the ends flat.

As wide as a paper clip.

2 Cut out a narrow strip from the center of the tape.

Cut to the wood

Looks like EARS!

3 Clamp the clothespin to the pull-tab on a can like this:

4 Lay your beam over a clothespin. Then push a pin through the exact center of the crossmarks. Leave the pin in.

Tape protects your finger

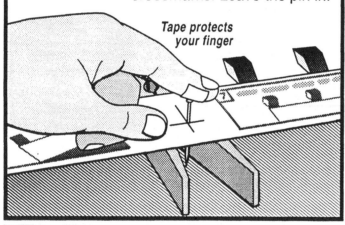

5 Balance your beam on the clothespin clipped on the can. The pin will rest between the "ears."

EARS

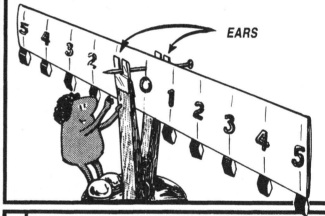

6 Bend out 2 paper clips just a little …

… then hang them from the 2 end loops like this.

7 Make the beam balance level by adding a folded tape tab to the lighter (higher) side.

LEVEL

Folded tape with sticky edge

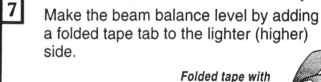

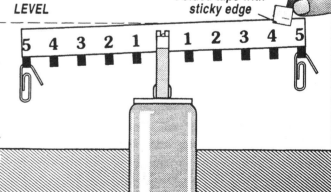

Copyright © 2004 by TOPS Learning Systems, Canby OR 97013. Reproduction limited to personal classroom use.

TOPS LEARNING SYSTEMS

Objective

To complete assembly of the math balance. To read and follow directions carefully.

Lesson Notes

1. The tape doesn't need to extend far beyond the clothespin. If the tape "ears" are too long, they are likely to curl and interfere with the free movement of the beam.

2. If using scissors of poor quality, your students may not be able to cleanly snip away the narrow center strip of tape. In this case, students can scrape it away with the scissors. They should remove it completely so the pivot pin can rest directly on the wood in step 5.

3. Either pop-top cans or small beverage bottles with *narrow* mouths can serve as bases for these balances. If a clothespin doesn't fit a bottle snugly, add tape around the nose of the clothespin.

4. It's important to push the pin through the **exact** center of the crossmarks. Some students may need help with this step. Propping the beam across the clothespin (or other "pincushion" surface, as discussed below) allows the pin to penetrate the beam while reducing the potential for punctured fingers. A couple of small squares of tape can further serve as a "thimble" to help protect sensitive fingers from pressure.

You can choose an alternative "pincushion" approach, which will be used later in these activities, by lightly affixing the following instruction over box 4 before you photocopy a class set. Find a list of quick and easy "pincushions" in the materials list for teaching notes 10.

> **4** Lay your beam over a "pincushion." Then push a pin through the exact center of the crossmark. Leave the pin in.
>
> Tape protects your finger.
>
> Foam cup "pincushion"

5. If a student's beam simply can't balance, it's probably upside down. The black tabs must be hanging down.

In general, the beam becomes more stable if the pin is moved higher on the vertical crossmark. This could work better for younger students, or if a lot of motion in the room is stirring up drafts, but readings will not be as precise. Lower pivots will be more sensitive, but become unstable if lower than the beam's center of gravity. This crossmark is a good compromise between stability and sensitivity. Older students might want to experiment.

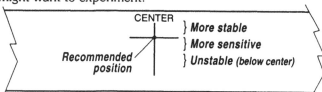

CENTER } More stable
} More sensitive
Recommended position } Unstable (below center)

6-7. You can center the beam without the paper clips, but it comes to rest more slowly, and may drift a bit off its equilibrium position. With **identical** paper clips lowering the center of gravity, the beam gains stability and will settle more quickly.

7. A "rider" will be needed to correct inevitable differences in weight between the two arms. A tab of masking tape, folded to leave a narrow sticky edge, is easy to adjust along the higher arm until the balance is just right. If this rider is simply too light to do the job, add more clear tape directly on the lighter arm until nearly balanced.

If the finished system isn't steady enough for younger kids to use easily, you might add some ballast (use sand or gravel) to make the bottle more tip-resistant. Further, you can fold a snippet of tape across the top of the masking tape ears on each side so the beam can't fall off the clothespin.

Evaluation

Is the pivot pin precisely centered? Does the beam swing freely, returning each time to a level position?

Materials

☐ The paper beam constructed in activity 1.

☐ Masking tape (clear tape may be substituted).

☐ Scissors.

☐ Two clothespins, or one clothespin and a soft "pincushion" surface such as an overturned styrofoam cup (see the materials for teaching notes 10).

☐ A straight pin.

☐ A pop-top can or soda bottle, glass or plastic.

☐ Paper clips of uniform size and weight. Use a standard size about this big:

☐ Optional ballast material: gravel, sand, beans, etc. See note 3.

PAPER CLIP BALANCING

1 Bend out the arms on 15 paper clips just a little.

Pull it out THIS FAR only.

2 Start with a *level* beam. Then add paper clips to make it balance level again.

3 Draw *7 different ways* to make your beam balance. Make an "X" for each clip.

4	5
	XXX

5	4	3	2	1		1	2	3	4	5

5	4	3	2	1		1	2	3	4	5

5	4	3	2	1		1	2	3	4	5

5	4	3	2	1		1	2	3	4	5

5	4	3	2	1		1	2	3	4	5

5	4	3	2	1		1	2	3	4	5

5	4	3	2	1		1	2	3	4	5

Copyright © 2004 by TOPS Learning Systems, Canby OR 97013. Reproduction limited to personal classroom use.

TOPS LEARNING SYSTEMS

Objective

To get acquainted with a math beam. To diagram various ways that paper clips balance on the beam.

Lesson Notes

1. Students tend to exaggerate this operation. Point out that the directions say to pull the "arms" out "just a little bit."

Banish all odd or mismatched paper clips from your classroom. This balance will not perform accurate math unless all paper clips have uniform weight.

2. As a matter of procedure, students should always check to see that their empty beams rest level **before** adding paper clips. They can correct any imbalance by adjusting the folded tape rider. It's also important that the beam not rub against the support system, which can prevent the beam from seeking a true balance.

Next, students should hang paper clips from the black tabs in combinations that make the beam balance level again. Mark the position of each clip by drawing an **X**, a dot, or some other mark in the appropriate box on the activity page. Each mark represents one clip. (Don't let students use numbers.)

Paper clips may be hung in clusters or chains, or any combination. Chains must not be so long they rest on the table top. Clusters should hang from a clip, and not from the tab, to reduce wear and tear on the paper. Be sure to count the "hanger" clip in the total.

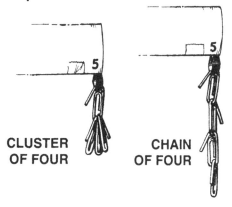

CLUSTER OF FOUR **CHAIN OF FOUR**

If the occasional tab does tear, a little tape quickly repairs the problem. The empty beam will need to be centered again with a bit of tape on the opposite arm.

3. There are many different combinations that balance the beam. Some students will be inclined to limit their investigation to a simple, symmetrical distribution for every answer. This is fine while they are becoming familiar with their beams. Later activities will require them to find uneven arrangements that balance.

Although students should not write numerals on their worksheet tabs, your more advanced students may discover with great triumph that their balances add and multiply like computers. This will become apparent in the next two activities.

Balances will last longer if students are responsible for their own. To this end, you might assign a specific place to keep their assembled balances and paper clips.

Answers

3. Here are just a few of *many* possible examples. You can quickly verify whether a solution is correct by checking the numerical totals on each side. Students will discover this quantitative connection in later activities, so don't rob them of the joy of discovery by introducing this concept yet.

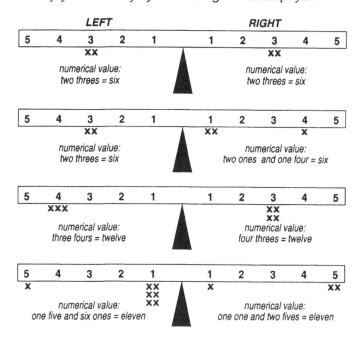

Materials

☐ The completed math balance.

☐ Paper clips of uniform size and weight.

BALANCE ADDITION

1 Be sure your empty beam balances level.

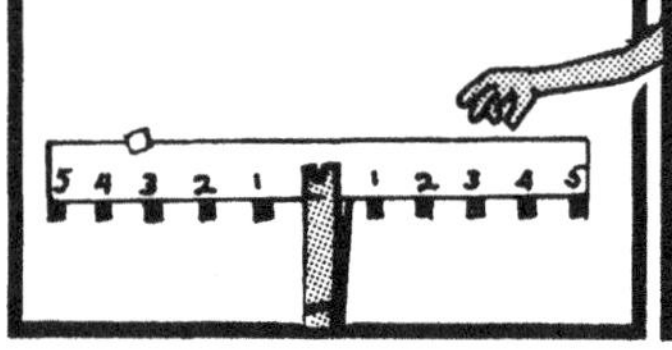

2 Add *just 2* clips to the *right* side to balance what is given (below) on the left side.

3 Mark your 2 paper clips. Then write an *equation* below each balance diagram. Make each way different.

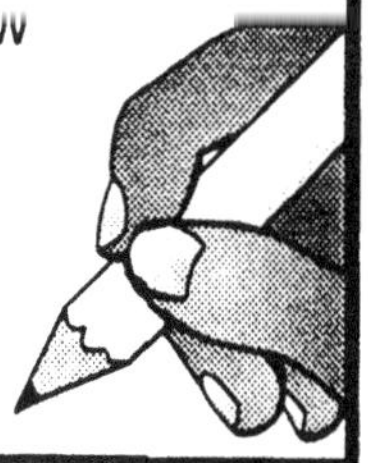

ADD TWO CLIPS:

| | | X
3 | | | | 1 | 2 | 3 | 4 | 5 |

| 3 | | = 3 |

ADD TWO CLIPS:

| | X
4 | | | | | 1 | 2 | 3 | 4 | 5 |

| 4 | | |

ADD TWO CLIPS:

| | X
4 | | | | | 1 | 2 | 3 | 4 | 5 |

| 4 | | |

ADD TWO CLIPS:

| X
5 | | | | | | 1 | 2 | 3 | 4 | 5 |

| 5 | | |

ADD TWO CLIPS:

| X
5 | | | | | | 1 | 2 | 3 | 4 | 5 |

| 5 | | |

Copyright © 2004 by TOPS Learning Systems, Canby OR 97013. Reproduction limited to personal classroom use.

TOPS LEARNING SYSTEMS

Objective

To understand that paper clips add up to equal sums on each arm of a balanced beam.

Introduction

For younger kids who don't yet have the word in their vocabularies, this activity opens a hands-on path to the definition of *equation*. But if students are perplexed when they are asked to write equations, tell them an equation is like a sentence written in numbers: it says the total value of everything on both sides of the equal sign must balance. Most simply, an equation says that "this equals that."

For example, $2 = 2$ and $4 + 2 = 6$ and $9 = 3 \times 3$ are all equations. In these examples, the values are the same on both sides of the equal sign. This very basic form of equation will serve for most problems presented in this book.

Ask your class to make up a few more samples. You might even challenge them to reach for "fancy" equations that include a math operation on both sides, such as $5 + 7 = 6 \times 2$.

Lesson Notes

1. Throughout these exercises, emphasize the importance of centering the beam each time students set up. If routine handling or tab repairs have caused the balance to tilt off level, students should adjust the tape rider before they work through the activities.

2-3. Some students may not initially understand what to do. Explain that they should hang the one *given* paper clip on the left arm first, then add two more to the other side to make the beam balance.

For younger students, you might write a sample problem on the board, and ask a volunteer to show how she would solve it. For a problem using tab "2" on the left side, draw this:

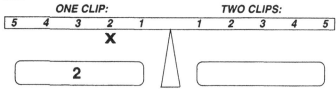

Ask your volunteer to hang the "given" weight: a *single* clip on tab 2 on the left side. Then ask for *two* clips on the right side to balance it. Students may immediately grasp that these would both go on tab "1" on the right side, or they may need to use a trial and error approach on their own balances. When the correct results have been obtained, ask what *equation* would describe these results, and write this in the box on the right side:

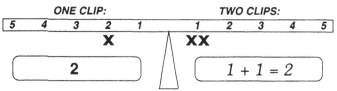

Answers

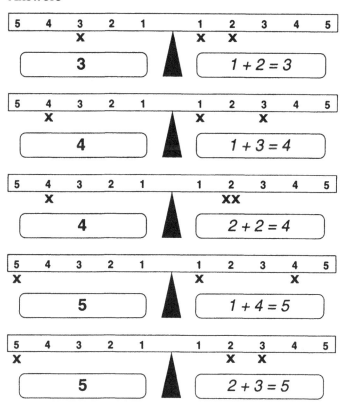

Materials

☐ A math balance.

☐ Paper clips of uniform size and weight.

BALANCE MULTIPLICATION

1 Start with a balanced beam.

2 Add paper clips **one at a time** to the two given tabs until your beam balances.

Use the tabs shown on each beam below.

3 Write a **different** multiplication equation in each box.

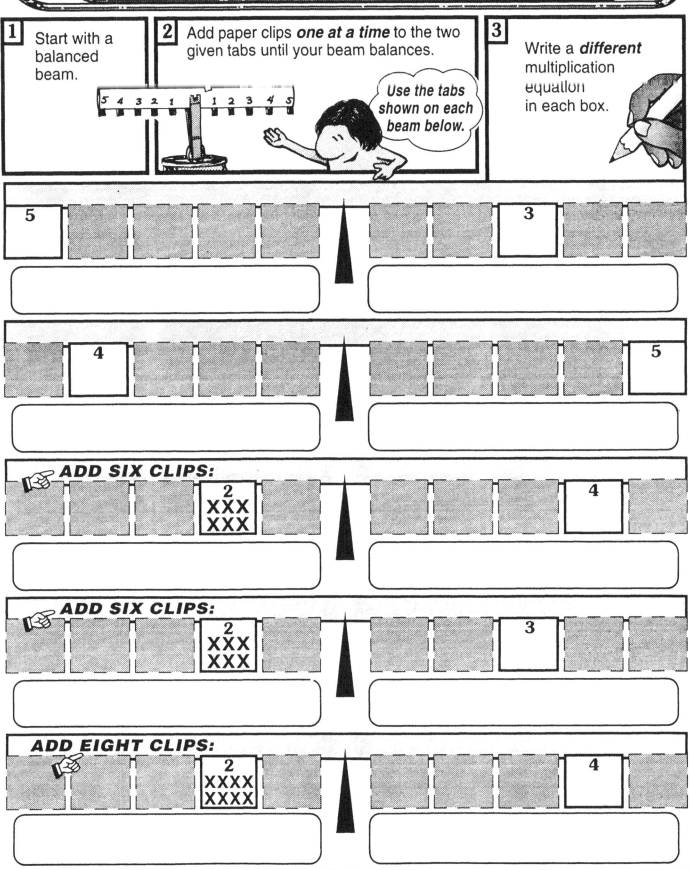

5 .... **3**

4 .... **5**

ADD SIX CLIPS: **2 XXX XXX** **4**

ADD SIX CLIPS: **2 XXX XXX** **3**

ADD EIGHT CLIPS: **2 XXXX XXXX** **4**

Copyright © 2004 by TOPS Learning Systems, Canby OR 97013. Reproduction limited to personal classroom use.

TOPS LEARNING SYSTEMS

Objective

To understand that paper clips multiply to equal products on each arm of a *balanced* beam.

Lesson Notes

2. Students work with just one given tab on each arm of the beam. They should add paper clips one at a time to whichever side requires more weight (see sequence below). In this manner, the beam finally reaches a state of balance.

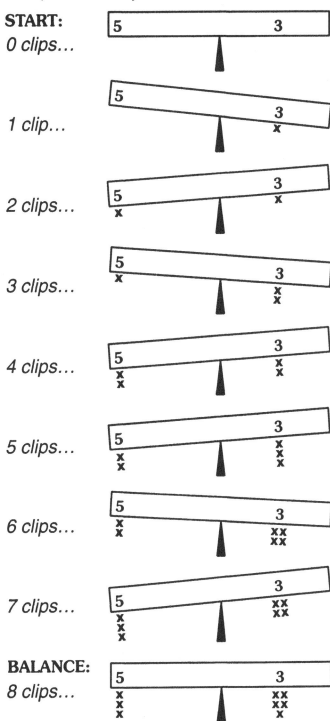

START:
0 clips...

1 clip...

2 clips...

3 clips...

4 clips...

5 clips...

6 clips...

7 clips...

BALANCE:
8 clips...

2. To achieve two different equations, students record the position and the number of clips hung on that tab:

5 x 3 = 15 → **3 x 5** = 15

Answers

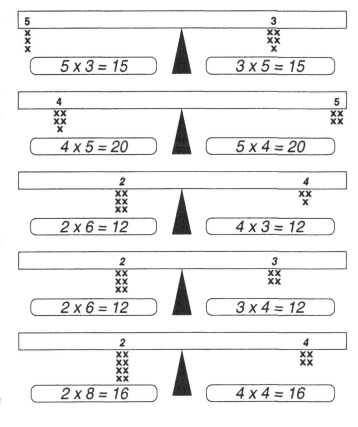

5		3
X		XX
X		XX
X		X

$5 \times 3 = 15$ $3 \times 5 = 15$

$4 \times 5 = 20$ $5 \times 4 = 20$

$2 \times 6 = 12$ $4 \times 3 = 12$

$2 \times 6 = 12$ $3 \times 4 = 12$

$2 \times 8 = 16$ $4 \times 4 = 16$

Extension

Brain bender: Set up a problem that demonstrates division. Use two different operations to demonstrate how to divide on your balance.

Start with a problem with large enough values to divide evenly, such as this example that divides by 2. Here are two possible ways to show this division:

ORIGINAL EQUATION: 2   4

$2 \times 8 = 16$ $4 \times 4 = 16$

One solution (number of clips are divided):

DIVIDE BY 2:   2   4
Remove half the clips:

$2 \times 8 \div 2 = 8$ $4 \times 4 \div 2 = 8$

Alternate solution (distance from pivot is divided):

DIVIDE BY 2:   2   1   2   4
Reduce the distance to the pivot by half:

$2 \div 2 \times 8 = 8$ $4 \div 2 \times 4 = 8$

Materials

☐ A math balance.

☐ Paper clips of uniform size and weight.

BALANCE PUZZLES

1 Add *2 clips* to the **left** arm of your beam as shown:

2 Add *just 3* clips to the right side to make it balance.

Make each answer different *!*

5 XX						**ADD THREE CLIPS:**				
						1	2	3	4	5

5 XX						**ADD THREE CLIPS:**				
						1	2	3	4	5

5 XX						**ADD THREE CLIPS:**				
						1	2	3	4	5

5 XX						**ADD THREE CLIPS:**				
						1	2	3	4	5

3 Add *2 clips* to the **left** arm of your beam as shown:

4 Add *just 4* clips to the right side to make it balance.

Make each way different.

5 XX						**ADD FOUR CLIPS:**				
						1	2	3	4	

5 XX						**ADD FOUR CLIPS:**				
						1	2	3	4	

5 XX						**ADD FOUR CLIPS:**				
						1	2	3	4	

5 XX						**ADD FOUR CLIPS:**				
						1	2	3	4	

Copyright © 2004 by TOPS Learning Systems, Canby OR 97013. Reproduction limited to personal classroom use.

TOPS LEARNING SYSTEMS

Objective

To gain further experience with balance beams and the mathematics of balancing.

Lesson Notes

2. Once students understand the mathematics of the balance beam, they tend to shift from physical activity (actually placing paper clips on the beam) to mental activity (writing number combinations that yield the desired result). This is the goal. As a result of concrete manipulations, students advance to a higher level of mental abstraction.

Those who experience difficulty in finding all four balance combinations can be helped by introducing the concept of symmetry. In the first four problems, notice how each solution is derived from the last by symmetry moves. Once the beam is placed in a state of balance, then clips that are moved in equal but opposite directions will maintain that balance.

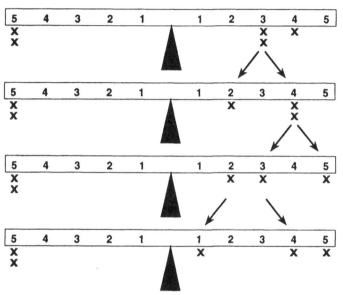

4. Notice that solutions to this last group of problems are restricted to the first four beam positions.

Answers

2.

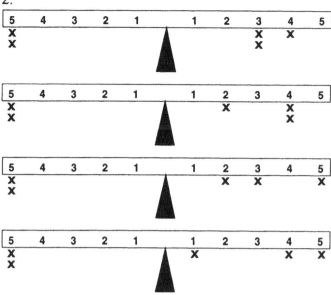

4. There are *five* possible solutions for this problem:

5	4	3	2	1		1	2	3	4
X							X		X
X							X		
							X		

5	4	3	2	1		1	2	3	4
X							X	X	
X							X	X	

5	4	3	2	1		1	2	3	4
X						X		X	
X								X	
								X	

5	4	3	2	1		1	2	3	4
X						X	X	X	X
X									

5	4	3	2	1		1	2	3	4
X						X		X	
X						X		X	

Materials

☐ A math balance.
☐ Paper clips of uniform size and weight.

MORE BALANCE PUZZLES

1 Add clips to the right arm to balance what is given on the left arm.

2 Write math equations in each pair of boxes to show that the beam balances.

Watch for instructions on the beams.

No more than ONE clip on a tab:

| | 4
XXX | 3
X | | | | 1 | 2 | 3 | 4 | 5 |

Add clips to only ONE tab:

| | 4
XX | | | 1
X | | 1 | 2 | 3 | 4 | 5 |

Add two clips to two different tabs:

| | 4
XX | 3
X | | 1
XXX | | 1 | 2 | | 4 | 5 |

Each tab must have the same number of clips:

| 5
XX
XX | | | | | 1 | 2 | 3 | 4 | |

Copyright © 2004 by TOPS Learning Systems, Canby OR 97013. Reproduction limited to personal classroom use.

TOPS LEARNING SYSTEMS

Objective

To practice expressing complex balance conditions as mathematical equations.

Lesson Notes

1-2. Some students will likely complete this activity without using a math balance. Others may need to use the balance to solve the puzzles. In either case, the exercise establishes a strong connection between mathematics and the nature of balancing beams.

If you are introducing students to equation-solving for the first time, you'll need to make them aware of a basic algebraic rule: perform any multiplication (or division) *before* adding (or subtracting).* Do the math in this equation to illustrate:

$$4x2 + 3x2 + 2x2 = 18$$

First perform the three multiplication operations, writing the products above the equation as shown:

$$\overset{8}{4}x2 + \overset{6}{3}x2 + \overset{4}{2}x2 = 18$$

When these three products are then added together, the total is 18. However, if we just work from left to right, straight through the equation, we would get 4 times 2 is 8, plus 3 is 11, times 2 is 22, plus 2 is 24, times two is 48. A very different answer than 18. It's obviously very important to work the equation in the correct order.

This sample problem can stay on the board as a model for students as they do the next few activities.

Extension

Ask students to demonstrate on their balances that 48 is not a reasonable answer to the sample problem above. *(The beam will begin to tilt down on the right as the mathematical value of the clips exceeds 18. Pushed to an amusing extreme, clips hanging in chains from tab 5 on the right arm will eventually be resting on the table.)*

Students might further make up a lengthy problem of their own and solve it correctly (multiply first, then add), and then incorrectly (do operations in any other order). Then they could demonstrate to the class or in small groups that the wrong answer won't balance.

* Note: There are circumstances in algebra where addition or subtraction should be done first, in which case these parts of the equation are enclosed in parentheses or brackets. Rather than giving your class this much information, which is irrelevant in these activities, simply mention that they will learn at another time that operations in brackets "ask" to be done first.

Answers

Each answer below is recorded in a left-to-right order, so numbers correspond to the physical placement of the paper clips on the beam. (Most students will follow this form automatically.) When multiplication is involved, the pre-algebra "times" symbol "x" is used, with the tab position written first, followed by the number of clips at that position. Accept any equation that is mathematically correct.

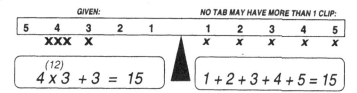

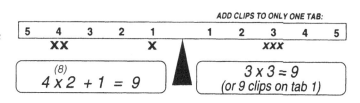

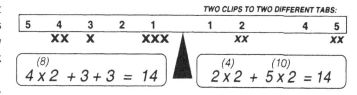

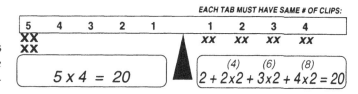

Materials

☐ A math balance.

☐ Paper clips of uniform size and weight.

DOES IT BALANCE?

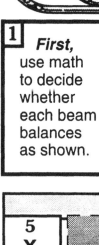

1 **First,** use math to decide whether each beam balances as shown.

2 Write your prediction. Will it balance?

(2) Predict: NO

3 **Finally,** add the given clips to your beam. Was your prediction correct? If not, find your math errors and circle them.

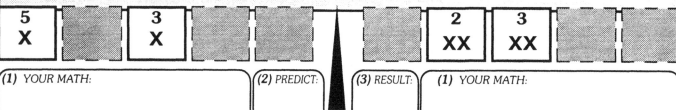

| 5 X | | 3 X | | | | 2 XX | 3 XX | |

| (1) YOUR MATH: | (2) PREDICT: | (3) RESULT: | (1) YOUR MATH: |

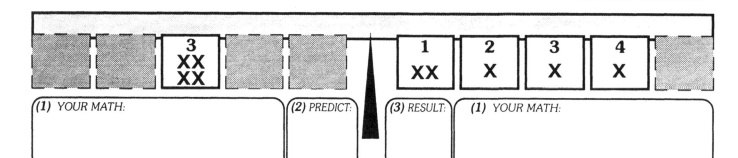

| | | 3 XX XX | | | | 1 XX | 2 X | 3 X | 4 X | |

| (1) YOUR MATH: | (2) PREDICT: | (3) RESULT: | (1) YOUR MATH: |

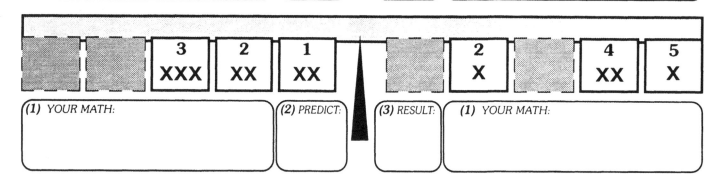

| | | 3 XXX | 2 XX | 1 XX | | | 2 X | | 4 XX | 5 X |

| (1) YOUR MATH: | (2) PREDICT: | (3) RESULT: | (1) YOUR MATH: |

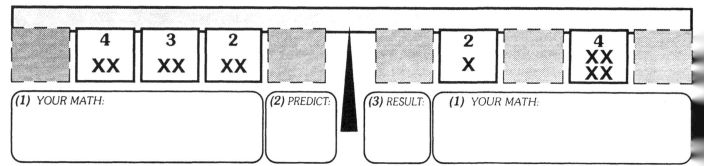

| | 4 XX | 3 XX | 2 XX | | | | 2 X | | 4 XX XX | |

| (1) YOUR MATH: | (2) PREDICT: | (3) RESULT: | (1) YOUR MATH: |

Copyright © 2004 by TOPS Learning Systems, Canby OR 97013. Reproduction limited to personal classroom use.

TOPS LEARNING SYSTEMS

Objective

To mathematically predict and then verify a state of balance or imbalance in a math beam.

Lesson Notes

This activity requires students to predict a state of balance (or imbalance) based on their mathematical calculations. Then they hang clips as given to verify by observation whether their prediction is correct. This process of thoughtful prediction followed by experimental verification is fundamental to doing science. Insist, therefore, that your students follow these steps in sequence:

1. calculate
2. predict
3. verify

Prediction means *speaking before;* in this case, students are speaking about an outcome before testing it. While these predictions are well-informed guesses, they are not required to be correct. Some students will be inclined to change their predictions if they find out they were wrong. Assure them that this activity is more about learning the math capabilities of balances, and about following instructions carefully, than it is about achieving correct answers. Students are asked to find and circle errors, but not to change their answers.

As in real science, mistakes are instructive if we pay attention to how, where, or why the error happened, which helps us avoid the same mistake again. Don't grade students down for wrong predictions. Rather, evaluation on this activity should be based on whether students grasped the concept of prediction, followed directions to the best of their ability, and wrote equations in the correct form.

Answers

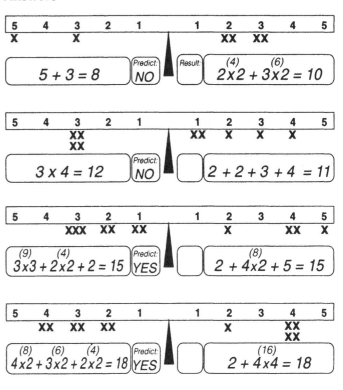

Materials

☐ A math balance.

☐ Paper clips of uniform size and weight.

WHICH WAY?

1	**2**	**3**
First, use math to decide how each beam will tilt.	Write your prediction. Will it ***balance***, tilt ***right***, or tilt ***left***?	***Finally,*** add the given clips to your beam.
		If your prediction is not correct, check your work to find out why.

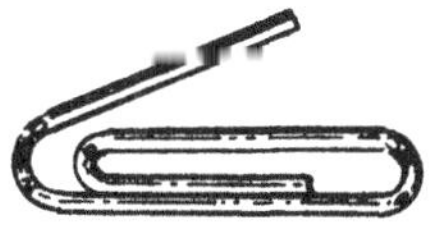

Beam 1: 4 X | 3 X | 2 XX | | | 2 X | | 4 XX

(1) YOUR MATH:

(2) PREDICT: *(3) RESULT:*   *(1) YOUR MATH:*

Beam 2: 5 XX XX | | 3 XXX | | | 1 X | 2 X | | 4 XXX XXX

(1) YOUR MATH:

(2) PREDICT: *(3) RESULT:*   *(1) YOUR MATH:*

Beam 3: 4 XXX | | 2 X | | | 2 XXX XXX | | 5 X

(1) YOUR MATH:

(2) PREDICT: *(3) RESULT:*   *(1) YOUR MATH:*

Beam 4: 5 X | 4 X | 3 XX | 2 X | 1 X | | 2 XX XXX | | 4 XX

(1) YOUR MATH:

(2) PREDICT: *(3) RESULT:*   *(1) YOUR MATH:*

Copyright © 2004 by TOPS Learning Systems, Canby OR 97013. Reproduction limited to personal classroom use.

TOPS LEARNING SYSTEMS

Objective

To mathematically predict and then verify the tilt of a math beam.

Lesson Notes

As in activity 8, remind students to follow these steps in sequence: *calculate, predict, verify.*

Extension

In this classroom demonstration, a student's weight is calculated by balancing on a two-by-four opposite another student of known weight. This "teeter-totter" system is analogous to a paper clip math balance: the numbered positions on the paper beam correspond to the distance that each person stands from the center pivot. The paper clips used on the beam correspond to the weight (in pounds or kilograms) of each student standing on the beam.

PREPARATION:

Mark an eight to ten foot two-by-four into 16 equal subdivisions. This is easily done by cutting string to the full length of the board, then folding it into half lengths, then again into quarter lengths, etc.

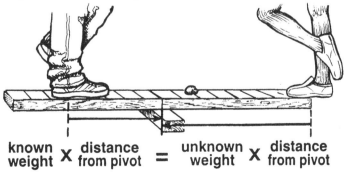

Use a block of wood or a brick as the pivot. If the beam will not balance at your center mark, add a flat rock or other appropriate weight as a "rider."

Use a bathroom scale to weigh students and check experimental results. Ask for volunteers who are not sensitive about being weighed in front of the class. This beam will be unstable when students stand on it because its center of gravity is far above the pivot. So assign "spotters" to assist. They should not, of course, support any weight, just provide a bracing hand if the "balancers" need it.

PRESENTATION:

Weigh one of two volunteers on the scale. Calculate the weight of the other using balance beam mathematics.

$$\text{known weight} \times \text{distance from pivot} = \text{unknown weight} \times \text{distance from pivot}$$

Answers

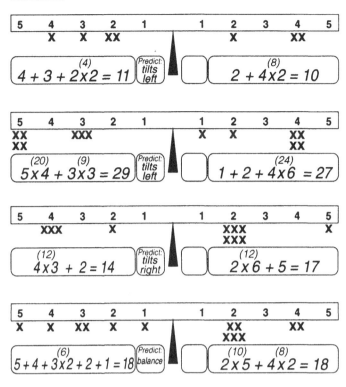

5	4	3	2	1		1	2	3	4	5
	X	X	XX				X		XX	

$$\overset{(4)}{4 + 3 + 2 \times 2} = 11 \quad \boxed{\substack{\text{Predict:}\\ \text{tilts}\\ \text{left}}} \quad \overset{(8)}{2 + 4 \times 2} = 10$$

5	4	3	2	1		1	2	3	4	5
XX		XXX				X	X		XX	
XX									XX	

$$\overset{(20)}{5 \times 4} + \overset{(9)}{3 \times 3} = 29 \quad \boxed{\substack{\text{Predict:}\\ \text{tilts}\\ \text{left}}} \quad \overset{(24)}{1 + 2 + 4 \times 6} = 27$$

5	4	3	2	1		1	2	3	4	5
XXX			X				XXX			X
							XXX			

$$\overset{(12)}{4 \times 3} + 2 = 14 \quad \boxed{\substack{\text{Predict:}\\ \text{tilts}\\ \text{right}}} \quad \overset{(12)}{2 \times 6} + 5 = 17$$

5	4	3	2	1		1	2	3	4	5
X	X	XX	X	X			XX		XX	
							XXX			

$$\overset{(6)}{5 + 4 + 3 \times 2} + 2 + 1 = 18 \quad \boxed{\substack{\text{Predict:}\\ \text{balance}}} \quad \overset{(10)}{2 \times 5} + \overset{(8)}{4 \times 2} = 18$$

Materials

☐ A math balance.

☐ Paper clips of uniform size and weight.

☐ The optionl extension activity requires extra materials. See above.

SHORT'N'LONG ARM BALANCING

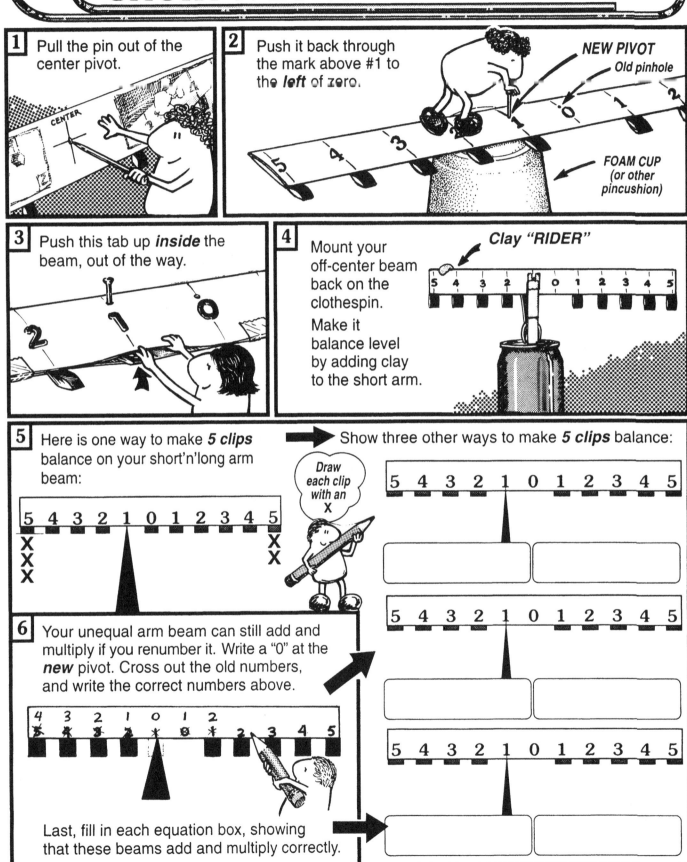

1 Pull the pin out of the center pivot.

2 Push it back through the mark above #1 to the *left* of zero.

NEW PIVOT
Old pinhole

FOAM CUP (or other pincushion)

3 Push this tab up *inside* the beam, out of the way.

4 Mount your off-center beam back on the clothespin.

Make it balance level by adding clay to the short arm.

Clay "RIDER"

5 Here is one way to make *5 clips* balance on your short'n'long arm beam:

Draw each clip with an X

Show three other ways to make *5 clips* balance:

6 Your unequal arm beam can still add and multiply if you renumber it. Write a "0" at the *new* pivot. Cross out the old numbers, and write the correct numbers above.

Last, fill in each equation box, showing that these beams add and multiply correctly.

Copyright © 2004 by TOPS Learning Systems, Canby OR 97013. Reproduction limited to personal classroom use.

TOPS LEARNING SYSTEMS

Objective

To recognize that the mathematical properties of an equal arm balance can be extended to a balance with unequal arms.

Lesson Notes

2. A styrofoam cup (or even a foam "packing peanut") makes a good "pin cushion," allowing the pin to be punched through the beam with relative ease. Other resilient materials, or even a gap between the wings of a clothespin, will work as well.

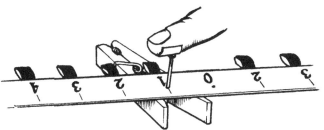

3. Since this is the last activity using this math beam, this tab could simply be snipped off. However, students may wish to take their math beams home intact for continued creative play.

4. The tape tab will not be heavy enough to counterbalance the longer arm, so clay is used here. When using clay riders to balance the shorter arm, students will encounter two variables in achieving balance – the size (weight) of the clay lumps, and the placement of the rider on the arm.

5. There are many ways to make 5 clips balance. Your students will probably find combinations different from our key.

Because the numbers on the beam no longer correspond to actual distances from the pivot, solutions such as these are best found by actual trial and error experimentation on the long'n'short arm balance.

6. Once distances to the center pivot are rewritten, students will discover that asymmetrical beams, like equal-arm beams, exhibit identical mathematical properties. A few students may have realized this even before renumbering their tabs.

Answers

5-6.

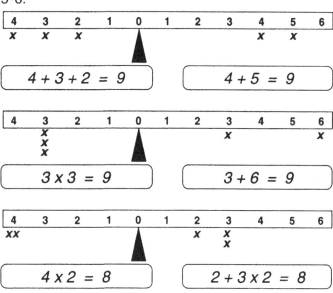

4	3	2	1	0	1	2	3	4	5	6
x	x	x						x	x	

4 + 3 + 2 = 9	4 + 5 = 9

4	3	2	1	0	1	2	3	4	5	6
	x						x			x
	x									
	x									

3 x 3 = 9	3 + 6 = 9

4	3	2	1	0	1	2	3	4	5	6
xx						x	x			
							x			

4 x 2 = 8	2 + 3 x 2 = 8

Materials

☐ A math balance.

☐ Paper clips of uniform size and weight.

☐ A lump of modelling clay.

☐ A styrofoam cup, foam "packing peanut," large rubber eraser, cork, or other "pincushion" material is optional. See step 2 above.

☐ Tape to protect fingers.

BUILD A PAPER BEAM BALANCE (1)

Copyright © 2004 by TOPS Learning Systems, Canby OR 97013.
Reproduction limited to purchaser's personal teaching use.

8 — **7** + **6** + **5** + **4** + **3** + **2** + **1** +

◇ CENTER ◇ FOLD ◇

1

START HERE: *Carefully* trim this paper along the outside dashed line.

2

Fold it in half **exactly** along the center line.

Keep these instructions on the OUTSIDE.

3

Fold up this half again so that all the edges meet. Hide this instruction box on the inside.

Fold up both edges together.

4

Fold up again so this box is inside. All the edges must meet evenly.

This is your THIRD fold.

5

Tape 3 times where shown to form a closed paper beam.

6

Make pinholes through the **3 circled crosses** on the other side.

7

Write your name here.

....

Objective

To construct a paper beam to use in a weighing balance. To read and follow directions carefully.

Lesson Notes

Before your students build their own weighing balances in this activity and the next, construct one yourself. This will familiarize you with the directions and provide a model for your students to follow.

1. Just like the math balance constructed in activities 1-2, this student activity page also folds into an actual balance beam. These directions are similar to the previous beam, so students should have an easy time completing their beams successfully.

2. When folded along this guideline, the long edges won't meet. They will "creep" together as the paper is folded into a beam in steps 3 and 4 .

Some students may fold the paper inward, covering the remaining instructions. The illustration directs students to fold the worksheet outward.

3. Both free edges must be folded **up** as illustrated, which brings step 4 into view. Students who fold their paper down from the top edge will see step 5 instead, and may skip step 4 altogether. Some may discover the mistake, however, when they find the taping required in step 5 doesn't make sense.

4. Again, the paper must be folded **up** to bring steps 5 through 7 into view.

6. Punch a pin through the 3 circled crosses, 1 in the middle, and 2 on the ends. (The smaller crosses above each number won't be used until activity 20.)

If your students are constructing this beam before the math beam, demonstrate how to easily push a pin through the beam by resting it on a foam cup or other cushioned surface. A couple of small squares of tape will help protect sensitive fingers from pressure. Teaching notes 10 offers other "pincushion" options.

7. The completed weighing beam should look like this:

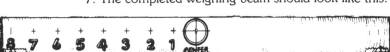

Materials

☐ A photocopy of the Paper Beam Balance (opposite page).

☐ Scissors.

☐ Clear tape.

☐ A straight pin.

☐ A styrofoam cup or other "pincushion." See step 6.

BUILD A PAPER BEAM BALANCE (2)

1 Fold a 3×5 index card in half both ways. Cut the long fold to the center.

Cut to center

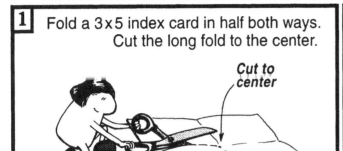

2 Fold up the tabs. Trim and tape.

a. Fold...   *b. Trim...*   *c. Tape.*

3 Unbend a paper clip. Tape the small end to the outside of your folded-up card.

4 Cut into the opposite end about 1 cm (the width of a paper clip). Fold up and tape.

b. Fold...

c. Tape.

a. Cut...

5 Repeat these steps to make a second weighing "pan."

6 Sharpen a pencil to a fine point. Use it to make the two *end* pinholes about as large as a pinhead.

ONLY THE 2 END HOLES.

Use a foam cup or other "pincushion."

7 Poke two more unbent paper clips through the enlarged holes. Stick a pin through the center.

+ 8 7 6 5 4 3 2 1 +

Small end

Large end

Put the pin back in.

8 Bend the paper clip on each weighing pan forward, then loop the free end.

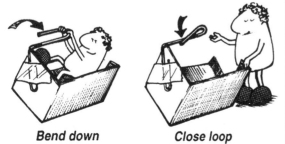

Bend down   *Close loop*

9 Mount your beam on a pin and clothespin. Hang a pan at each end, then center the beam with a folded tape rider.

A finished balance!

tape "ears"   tape rider

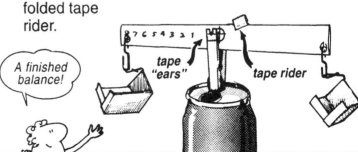

Copyright © 2004 by TOPS Learning Systems, Canby OR 97013. Reproduction limited to personal classroom use.

TOPS LEARNING SYSTEMS

Objective

To complete construction of the weighing balance. To read and follow directions carefully.

Lesson Notes

6. Students who try to accomplish this step with a dull pencil will probably "dog-ear" the corners of the beam, and may break through the top of the cup, as well. A very sharp pencil is a must.

Place the point on the pinhole, then rotate the pencil between your fingers like a drill. This will produce a clean, well-defined hole. Take care not to make these holes too large. Drilling them to about the size of a pinhead is large enough to allow a paper clip "hook" to rotate easily, without wobbling from side to side.

7. In general, the beam becomes more stable as you place the pivot pin higher, and more unstable (but more sensitive) as you place the pin lower.

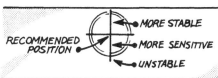

The intersection of the cross marks is only a recommended compromise between stability and sensitivity. Make adjustments up or down the vertical line as necessary.

8. The paper clips should be bent forward to right angles so that the pans will hang level. The closed loops keep the pans from inadvertently falling off while students are adding or removing weights.

9. The clothespin support system used here is the same as used for the math balance. If you have not already constructed that balance, see teaching notes 2, steps 1-3 for details.

Depending on how much tape is used to construct each weighing pan, one is probably a little heavier than the other. The tape rider corrects for this. A folded tab of tape with a small sticky edge left exposed makes frequent recentering easy. Whenever the pans are switched, the rider will need to be moved accordingly. (A paper clip, which can crease the beam and compromise its rigidity, is *not* a good substitute.)

It's also important that the beam swing freely in order work well. It must not rub against the supporting clothespin. If a student begins to get answers that are inconsistent or don't make sense, the beam may be hitting the support.

Evaluation

Is the beam folded neatly and taped where instructed? Does the balance level itself again if tipped off center? Do the pans hang level so that added weights won't spill out? Do the paper clip hooks rotate freely, allowing the pans to remain level as the beam is tilted from side to side?

Materials

☐ The paper beam constructed in activity 11.

☐ Two 3 x 5 index cards.

☐ Scissors.

☐ Clear tape.

☐ Paper clips of uniform size and weight.

☐ Masking tape to make the moveable rider.

☐ An optional styrofoam cup or other "pincushion," as in activity 10.

☐ A suitable base for the beam. Students may use the same base established for the math beam, or make a new one from a soda can or bottle, clothespin, and straight pin. See activity 2 if students have not made a math balance.

BALANCE EQUATIONS

1
Center your beam and count what balances.
Estimate halves or quarters as necessary.

10 thumb tacks = [____] paper clips

10 paper clips = [____] popcorn

10 popcorn = [____] lentils

10 lentils = [____] rice

2
Fill in these boxes. Don't weigh again, just divide by 10.

1 thumb tack = [____] paper clips

1 paper clip = [____] popcorn

1 popcorn = [____] lentils

1 lentil = [____] rice

3

Plug in values from step 2.

Multiply by unit conversion factors to solve each equation …

…then check each answer on your balance.

a. **1** thumb tack = **?** popcorn

$$\frac{1 \text{ thumb tack}}{1} \times \frac{\boxed{} \text{ paper clips}}{1 \text{ thumb tack}} \times \frac{\boxed{} \text{ popcorn}}{1 \text{ paper clip}} = \boxed{} \text{ popcorn}$$

a. *balance check:*

b. **1** paper clip = **?** lentils

b. *balance check:*

c. **1** popcorn = **?** rice

c. *balance check:*

Copyright © 2004 by TOPS Learning Systems, Canby OR 97013. Reproduction limited to personal classroom use.

TOPS LEARNING SYSTEMS

Objective

To make weight comparisons on a balance and thereby generate simple mathematical relationships.

Lesson Notes

1. As in all activities, students should first center their beams; move the tape rider as necessary.

Your thumb tacks and paper clips may weigh differently than ours. Since these items are uniform in your own classrooms, you may find that student answers vary less widely from each other than from our answer key.

Popcorn, lentil and rice varieties may also vary. You can increase internal consistency in the seeds you buy, without altering average weights, by directing students to pick out and discard seeds that are exceptionally small AND exceptionally large in EQUAL numbers. Half seeds and broken fragments should also be removed.

Demonstrate how to minimize counting errors by sorting multiple objects into smaller groups of equal size. Then count the groups, multiply by the number of objects per group, and add any remainder.

3. This step introduces an extremely useful problem-solving skill called unit analysis (also dimensional analysis). The strategy is simple. Start with numbers and units that you know. Then multiply by unit conversion factors (fancy ways to write "one"), so that units cancel to the answer you're looking for. What you start with and what you end with amounts to the same value, but stated in different units. Multiplying by one changed the form of the number, but not its value.

Begin with these dollar-and-cents examples. Given three basic equations, use unit analysis to derive new equations.

1 dollar = 4 quarters. Thus, $\dfrac{1\ dollar}{4\ quarters}$ and $\dfrac{4\ quarters}{1\ dollar} = 1$

1 quarter = 5 nickels. Thus, $\dfrac{1\ quarter}{5\ nickels}$ and $\dfrac{5\ nickels}{1\ quarter} = 1$

1 nickel = 5 pennies. Thus, $\dfrac{1\ nickel}{5\ pennies}$ and $\dfrac{5\ pennies}{1\ nickel} = 1$

Multiply by the unit conversion factors above to solve each problem below.

1 dollar = ? nickels

$$\frac{1\ dollar}{1} \times \frac{4\ quarters}{1\ dollar} \times \frac{5\ nickels}{1\ quarter}$$
$$= 20\ nickels$$

1 quarter = ? pennies

$$\frac{1\ quarter}{1} \times \frac{5\ nickels}{1\ quarter} \times \frac{5\ pennies}{1\ nickel}$$
$$= 25\ pennies$$

1 dollar = ? pennies

$$\frac{1\ dollar}{1} \times \frac{4\ quarters}{1\ dollar} \times \frac{5\ nickels}{1\ quarter} \times \frac{5\ pennies}{1\ nickel}$$
$$= 100\ pennies$$

Be sure students understand they are to do the math *first*, before checking answers on their balances. Students should expect variations in their answers, since there are weight variations in the seeds.

Answers

1. Answers depend on materials used:

> 10 thumb tacks = 13 1/2 paper clips
> 10 paper clips = 24 1/2 popcorns
> 10 popcorns = 33 lentils
> 10 lentils = 26 rice

2. Dividing each equation by 10:

> 1 thumb tack = 1.35 paper clips
> 1 paper clip = 2.45 popcorns
> 1 popcorn = 3.3 lentils
> 1 lentil = 2.6 rice

3. Model calculations based on answers above:

$$\frac{1\ thumb\ tack}{1} \times \frac{1.35\ paper\ clips}{1\ thumb\ tack} \times \frac{2.45\ popcorns}{1\ paper\ clip}$$
$$= 3.31\ popcorns$$

Balance check: 3+ popcorns

$$\frac{1\ paper\ clip}{1} \times \frac{2.45\ popcorn}{1\ paper\ clip} \times \frac{3.3\ lentils}{1\ popcorn}$$
$$= 8.09\ lentils$$

Balance check: 8 lentils

$$\frac{1\ popcorn}{1} \times \frac{3.3\ lentils}{1\ popcorn} \times \frac{2.6\ rice}{1\ lentils}$$
$$= 8.58\ rice$$

Balance check: 9 rice

Materials

☐ The balance constructed in activities 11 and 12.

☐ Paper clips of uniform size and weight. We used Acco #1 paper clips, purchased in 2004, as our paper-clip weighing standard. Expect different results (in this lesson and those that follow), if you use a different brand with a different uniform weight. *Note: Manufacturers redesign their clips occasionally. Watch for variations among clips purchased at different times.*

☐ Thumb tacks or push pins of uniform size and weight that are somewhat heavier than your paper clips. Check this in advance.

☐ Three kinds of seeds: popcorn, lentils, and long-grain rice. (Our calculations are based on white rice.) For most consistent results, eliminate seeds that are exceptionally large and small in each category (see lesson note 1 above).

☐ A calculator.

PAPER CLIP WEIGHING (1)

1 Use your balance to weigh each item in paper clips:

You may write **paper clips** *like this:*

Record **10+** *if it weighs a little* **more** *than 10.*

Write **10⁻** *if it weighs a little* **less** *than 10.*

Use **10½** *if somewhere in between.*

1 penny = ... **p.c.**

1 sheet notebook paper = ...

1 nickel = ...

1 index card = ...

2 Weigh at least four other things in your classroom. Write your answers in paper clips.

a.

b.

c.

d.

Write on the back if you wish to weigh more items.

3 Find the weight of a rice grain in paper clips. Show your math.

What PART of me equals ONE of you?

Copyright © 2004 by TOPS Learning Systems, Canby OR 97013. Reproduction limited to personal classroom use.

TOPS LEARNING SYSTEMS

Objective

To weigh common objects using a paper clip weight standard.

Lesson Notes

1-2. Objects rarely weigh a whole number of paper clips. Students should use "+" and "−" symbols or fractions as ways of expressing values that lie in between. (In activity 15, students will weigh all items again to the nearest *tenth* of a clip. Those who weigh nonuniform objects of unique weight should keep track of them.)

2. Anything that fits into the pan (or rests across it), is appropriate to weigh. Other objects might include nails, pencils or crayons, erasers, bottle caps, chalk, corks or rubber stoppers, cotton balls, marbles or beads, buttons, key chains or rings, bobby pins, pen caps, packing peanuts…. (Note: Avoid using edible nuts, as even physical contact can cause dangerous allergic reactions in some individuals.)

Some kids enjoy the added drama of guessing first how much an object will weigh, then testing their predictions.

3. Until now, students have been weighing things heavier than paper clips. So how do you weigh something that's way lighter? Encourage students to puzzle this out on their own and use their math skills!

Answers

Expect variation. Results depend on materials used.

1. 1 penny = 6⁺ p.c.
    1 sheet of notebook paper = 7 p.c.
    1 nickel = 12 ½ p.c.
    1 3x5 index card = 4⁺ p.c.

2. A few of many possible comparisons:
    1 quarter = 14 p.c.
    1 dime = 5 ½ p.c.
    1 clothespin = 17 p.c.
    1 bottle cap = 5 ½ p.c.

3. 21 rice grains = 1 p.c.
    Thus, 1 rice gr. = 1/21 p.c. = .048 p.c.

Materials

☐ A paper beam balance.

☐ Paper clips of uniform size and weight.

☐ Specified items to weigh: a new penny (minted after 1982), a sheet of paper, a nickel, and a 3x5 index card.

☐ Optional items to weigh: see suggestions in step 2, above. When collecting a category of items (such as buttons), select for uniformity.

☐ A calculator.

Extension

Draw and label these 6 schematic "objects." Construct a table of **mass** (number of dots), **area** (number of squares) and **density** (dots/square) with your students.

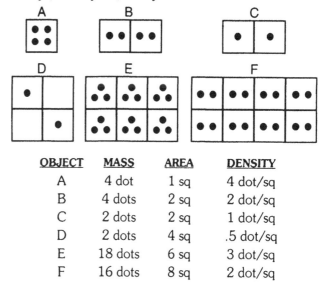

OBJECT	MASS	AREA	DENSITY
A	4 dot	1 sq	4 dot/sq
B	4 dots	2 sq	2 dot/sq
C	2 dots	2 sq	1 dot/sq
D	2 dots	4 sq	.5 dot/sq
E	18 dots	6 sq	3 dot/sq
F	16 dots	8 sq	2 dot/sq

A: Which object has the most mass? *(E)*

Which object has the most area ? *(F)*

Which object has the greatest density ? *(A)*

Which objects have equal mass ? *(A and B, C and D)*

Which objects have equal area? *(B and C)*

Which objects have equal density? *(B and F)*

Note: **Mass** is how much stuff (protons, neutrons and electrons) something is made of. **Weight** is how strongly this matter is attracted by gravity. On the Earth's surface, where the acceleration of gravity is everywhere about equal, mass and weight are interchangeable. We can say, for example, that 28.4 grams (a mass measurement) equals 1 ounce (a weight measurement). But on the moon, this much mass weighs only 1/6 ounce. And in space, 28.4 grams weighs 0 ounces – nothing at all! So weight changes with gravity, but mass remains constant.

B: Consider the very different compositions of a small, heavy rock and a large, light, packing "peanut." Which item in the table above corresponds to each of these materials?

The foam peanut corresponds to object D (more volume, less mass, lower density), while the rock is most like object A (less volume, more mass, higher density.)

C: On your balance, compare equal volumes (level teaspoons) of salt, sugar and sand. (Investigate other granulated products -- pepper, cornmeal, etc., as well). Order these heaviest to lightest.

Heavy to light: sand, salt, sugar, cornmeal, pepper, ….

D: Calculate the *densities* of salt, sugar and sand in paper clips per level teaspoon. Measure to the nearest tenth of a paper clip (after completing activity 15).

sugar: *D = 6.9 paper clips per level teaspoon*
salt: *D = 9.9 p.c. / tsp*
sand: *D = 12.7 p.c. / tsp*

PAPER CLIP WEIGHING (2)

1 Carefully cut out the *PAPER CLIP STRIP* at the bottom of this page.

2 Cut parallel strips off the end until it weighs *exactly* 1 paper clip.

paper clip

Cut **THIN** strips, **WITH** the lines. If you cut too much, you'll have to start over.

3 Divide this "paper clip strip" into **10 equal parts**.

Numbers on lined paper will help you do this.

4 Cut your strip to make these *paper clip fractions*.

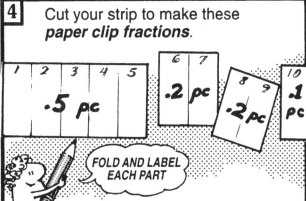

.5 pc   .2 pc   .2 pc   .1 pc

FOLD AND LABEL EACH PART

5 Weigh all items from activity 14 again, to the nearest ¹/₁₀ paper clip.

1 penny = _____   _____ = _____

1 notebook paper = _____ } your items _____ = _____

1 nickel = _____   _____ = _____

1 index card = _____   _____ = _____

7 Tape an unbent paper clip to the base of your balance. Store your paper weights here.

6 How are these weights different from what you found before?

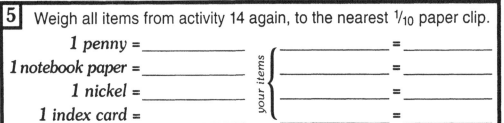

PAPER CLIP STRIP

Copyright © 2004 by TOPS Learning Systems, Canby OR 97013. Reproduction limited to personal classroom use.

TOPS LEARNING SYSTEMS

Objective

To develop and use a system of weight measure that's accurate to a tenth of a paper clip. To read and follow directions carefully.

Lesson Notes

2. You might want to make a few extra photocopies of the strip at the bottom of the activity page, so that students who cut theirs too short can try again with a new one. Consider challenging students with **Extension A** (at right) as they cut. Or use it in a class demonstration.

3. A common error is to count the number of lines instead of the number of spaces. Writing numbers in the notebook paper spaces, as shown, reduces this confusion. Students should angle their weighing strips so the top left and top right corners meet the beginning and end of the numbered spaces on the notebook paper. The blue lines on the notebook paper will then meet the edge of the weighing strip at tenths of its total length.

Answers

5. Again, results depend on materials used. Even the weights of these uniform U.S. coins may differ if your paper clips are lighter or heavier than ours.

specified items:

> 1 new penny = 6.3 p.c.
>
> 1 notebook paper = 7.0 p.c.
>
> 1 nickel = 12.6 p.c.
>
> 1 index card = 4.2 p.c.

optional items:

> 1 quarter = 14.2 p.c.
>
> 1 dime = 5.7 p.c.
>
> 1 clothespin = 16.9 p.c.
>
> 1 bottle cap = 5.4 p.c.

6. These weights are accurate to the nearest tenth of a paper clip, while answers in Activity 14 are accurate to only the nearest quarter or half paper clip.

Extensions

A. As kids are trimming their strip of paper to match the weight of a paper clip, they can come very close to the correct size by weighing the cut-offs instead of discarding them. Challenge students to discover this nifty technique (which also reduces the chance of trimming off too much paper) when they start cutting in step 2. Alternately, this technique also makes an interesting demonstration.

Place the cut-offs in the other weighing pan with the paper clip as you remove them. When the beam balances, these snippets of paper equal the amount of paper that must still be cut off the long strip to equal the paper clip.

B. Do U.S. pennies minted before 1982 weigh the same as pennies minted after 1982? Write a report that includes the idea of density.

In 1982, the U.S. began minting pennies that were nearly 2 p.c. lighter, but with the same size (volume) as before. Most of the more expensive higher density copper was replaced by cheaper lower density aluminum.

C. Is your balance sensitive enough to detect weight loss in pennies due to wear?

Counterbalancing a group of ten worn pennies against an equal number of unworn pennies will allow students to detect weight differences down to 0.01 p.c. (And differences will be more significant than that.) Pennies minted before and after 1982, of course, must not be mixed.

D. A nickel has a mass of 5.0 grams, while a post-1982 penny weighs precisely half as much (2.5 grams). Create a gram system of weight measure based these coins.

Knowing the weigh of these coins in paper clips, students might calculate a paper-clip gram equivalency, then develop a coin and paper system of gram weights similar to the paper clip system developed before. The Acco Brand #1 clips we purchased in 2004 resulted in these remarkably simple conversions:

> *1 paper clip = 0.4 grams*
>
> *1 gram = 2.5 paper clips*

E. Waterproof your weighing pans with aluminum foil. Using a 10 mL graduated cylinder, water, and an eyedropper, investigate the relationship between milliliters and grams. What can you discover?

This investigation leads to the fundamental metric relationship: 1 mL of water has a mass of 1 gram. The metric systems is so defined that water, by definition, has a density of 1 g/mL. (Water by definition has a specific gravity of 1. The density of other liquids are generally understood in terms of this standard.)

Materials

☐ A paper beam balance.

☐ Paper clips of uniform size and weight.

☐ Scissors.

☐ Items to weigh: Use the same specified and optional objects as in activity 14.

PAPER SQUARE WEIGHTS

1 *Cut* out the squares below along the *dashed* lines. *Fold* along the *solid* lines so the numbers still show.

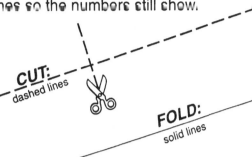

CUT:
dashed lines

FOLD:
solid lines

2 Weigh a paper clip to the nearest ¼ *paper square*. Be accurate.

$$1 \text{ p.c.} = \boxed{} \text{ sq.}$$

3 You've previously determined the weight of a penny in paper clips. How many paper squares is this?

$$1 \text{ penny} = \text{p.c.} \times \frac{\text{sq.}}{\text{p.c.}}$$

4 Weigh a penny in *paper squares* to confirm your calculation. Use *only* your own 28 squares and some clay.

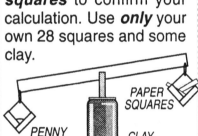

PENNY
PAPER SQUARES
CLAY

Tell how you did this.

4

SAVE YOUR SQUARES

PAPER SQUARES
Cut dashed lines only.

½ ¼ ¼ 2 2 4 4
10 10 10 10 10 4

10 10 10 10 10

Copyright © 2004 by TOPS Learning Systems, Canby OR 97013. Reproduction limited to personal classroom use.

TOPS LEARNING SYSTEM

Objective

To develop a weighing system based on paper squares. To multiply by a unit conversion factor that changes paper-clip weight measure to paper-squares, and confirm this calculation by experiment.

Lesson Notes

1. Students should cut along the dotted lines, then fold along the solid lines to create a system of labeled weights. Numbers should remain visible on the outside of each block for easy identification.

2-3. Notice that the equality in step 2 establishes the unit conversion factor in step 3. In general, any equation $x = y$ may be restated in terms of unit conversion factors: $1 = y/x$ and $x/y = 1$.

3. Some students may pool their paper squares for the purpose of weighing the penny directly. While this is a fine means of double-checking their answer, the original problem remains: how to weigh the penny using *only* 28 squares plus clay.

Answers

2. 1 p.c. = $8\frac{1}{4}$ sq.

3. 1 penny = 6.3 p.c. x 8.25 sq. / 1 p.c. = 52 sq.

4. First, weigh the penny in squares *plus* clay. Then weigh the clay alone, and add the two together for the total weight:

$$
\begin{aligned}
1 \text{ penny} &= 28 \text{ sqs. } + \text{ clay} \\
\text{clay} &= 24.5 \text{ sq.} \\
1 \text{ penny} &= 28 \text{ sqs. } + 24.5 \text{ sq.} \\
&= 52.5 \text{ sq.}
\end{aligned}
$$

There are other ways to solve this problem:

(1) Put enough clay in one pan to exactly balance a penny in the other. Then divide the clay and weigh the parts in paper squares. The total equals the weight of the penny. And...

(2) Create additional 10-square weights from lumps of clay. Use these plus the original paper squares to weigh the penny directly.

Extension

A. The following items were weighed to the nearest tenth of a paper clip in activity 15. Convert each weight mathematically to paper squares, then confirm your calculations on a balance with paper squares and clay.

> a sheet of notebook paper
> a nickel
> an index card

B. Weigh 0, 1, 2 and 3 *paper clips* with *paper squares*. Graph your data. Extrapolate (extend) your graph line.

Materials

☐ A paper beam balance.

☐ A set of weighing squares, cut from the bottom of this activity sheet. If you duplicate these using standard 20 pound copy paper, then your class results should approximate our answer key.

☐ Scissors.

☐ A paper clip.

☐ A post-1982 penny.

☐ A lump of modeling clay.

☐ A calculator.

PINTO BEAN STATISTICS

1 Randomly select 21 pinto beans from a bowl with your eyes closed.
Place one on each black oval, arranged from smallest to largest by how big they look.

SMALLEST ➤ — — — — — — — — — — — — — — — — — — — ➤ LARGEST

2 Weigh each pinto to the nearest ¼ **paper square** and record this weight in each box **above**. Start with the smallest (left end) and work toward the largest (right end). It's OK if weights don't always increase.

3 Mark an "X" for each bean on the grid below.

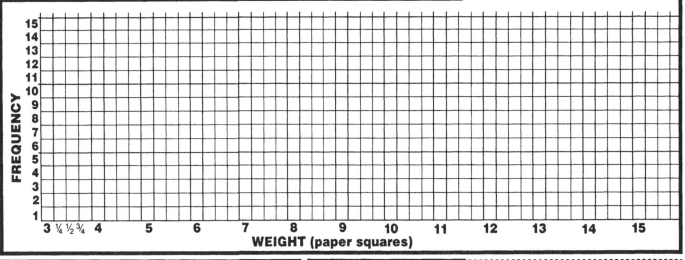

FREQUENCY (y-axis: 1 through 15)
WEIGHT (paper squares) (x-axis: 3 ¼ ½ ¾ 4 5 6 7 8 9 10 11 12 13 14 15)

4 Find the *mode*, *median* and *mean* weight in your sample of 21 beans.

MODE: *The most frequent weight. It appears more often than any other.*	
MEDIAN: *The central weight. It has an equal number of beans above and below it.*	
MEAN: *The average weight. Add all the weights and divide by 21 (the total number of beans).*	

your math:

5 Add more X's to your bean distribution from the grids of others:

MY RESULTS ARE POOLED WITH:

....

....

....

....

What happens to the distribution as the bean pool grows?

6 How many p.c. does a bean weigh? Answer on the back. Include unit conversion factors in your answer.

? 📎 = 🫘

Copyright © 2004 by TOPS Learning Systems, Canby OR 97013. Reproduction limited to personal classroom use.

TOPS LEARNING SYSTEMS

Objective

To weigh individual pinto beans in paper squares and graph a distribution profile.

Lesson Notes

1. This selection process should be random (eyes closed). Otherwise students may choose bigger beans and skew their results.

2. These 21 beans arranged by apparent size facilitate an orderly weighing process. The smallest bean can be weighed first, and then the next, and the next, with only minor additions or subtractions of paper weights.

Students are detecting subtle weight differences of just $1/4$ paper square. They should be certain their balance is centered dead level by adjusting the rider, then add precisely enough paper weight to return the beam to dead level again.

Accurately weighing 21 beans requires skill and patience. If younger students lose focus, you might lower the requirement to just 11 beans. We recommend assigning an uneven number so there will always be just one "median" bean in step 4.

When students are satisfied that they have recorded accurate weights, it's OK to return the beans to the bowl.

3. Each bean weight recorded in step 2 should be assigned a corresponding "X" in the lowest empty block on the grid. These "X's" stack into columns, forming a histogram of weight vs frequency, as students tally multiple beans with the same weight.

5. Each student's distribution profile will have a unique look, like an irregular city skyline with gaps between buildings. As students pool their results, this skyline will smooth out to some extent, but a classic "haystack" distribution curve is not probable without increasing the pool to thousands of beans.

Extension

A. What's the smallest pinto bean that you can find? The largest? Go for a record!

B. Copy and tape together as many blank grids as needed to develop a class distribution of pinto beans. How large is your bean pool? Is there any evidence of bias in this distribution?

You may notice a tendency for students to prefer to answer with whole numbers like 6 or 7, and avoid fractional answers, especially 6.75, rounding instead to 6.5 or 7.0.

C. Investigate the weight distribution of popcorn seeds. Compare it to your work with pinto beans.

Answers

2. Here is one result (among millions) for 21 randomly selected beans. All weights are in paper squares:
4.0, 4.25, 4.25, 4.5, 4.75, 6.5, 6.0, 6.25, 6.5, 6.5, 6.5, 6.25, 6.75, 6.75, 6.5, 6.75, 7.75, 7.75, 8.0, 7.75, 8.75

3. This raw data graphs as follows:

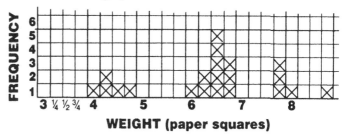

4. mode = 6.5 sq. (most frequent weight)
median = 6.5 sq. (middle weight)
mean = 6.3 sq. (average weight = 133/21 = 6.3)

5. Students should collaborate and combine data. With a larger bean pool, the distribution becomes somewhat more regular, especially near the mode. There may be fewer gaps. With a large enough bean pool, the overall shape of the x's may look less like a series of sharp peaks and canyons, and more like a mountain.

6. *Students should recall from the previous activity how many paper squares a paper clip weighs. Here's a model answer based on materials we used.*
1 paper clip = 8.25 paper squares
1 p.c. / 8.25 sq. = 1
This conversion factor may be applied to pinto beans in various ways:
pinto bean(mode, median) = 6.5 sq x 1 p.c. / 8.25 sq. = .79 p.c.
pinto bean(mean) = 6.3 sq x 1 p.c. / 8.25 sq. = .76 p.c.
pinto bean(smallest) = 4.0 sq x 1 p.c. / 8.25 sq. = .48 p.c.
pinto bean(largest) = 8.25 sq x 1 p.c. / 8.25 sq. = 1.06 p.c.
pinto bean(range) ≈ .75 ± .25 p.c.

Materials

☐ A paper beam balance.
☐ A bag of pinto beans and a bowl or equivalent.
☐ The paper square weights from activity 16.
☐ A calculator.

SQUARES AND RECTANGLES

1 Get a **SQUARES AND RECTANGLES** page. Carefully cut out all the shapes, and the small ruler.

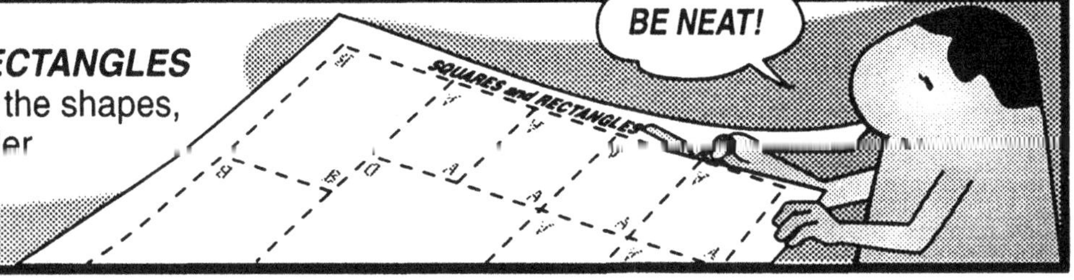

BE NEAT!

2 Measure each shape with the small ruler. Then multiply to find the area.

	LENGTH (in units)	x	WIDTH (in units)	=	AREA (in square units)
A =	units	x	units	=	sq units
B =		x		=	
C =		x		=	
D =		x		=	
E =		x		=	

3 Find out how many squares and rectangles balance each other. Use whole numbers only.

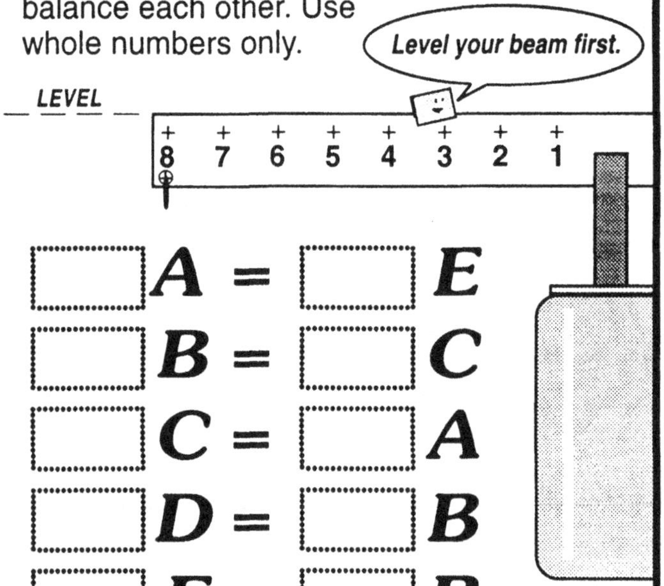

Level your beam first.

LEVEL

+8 +7 +6 +5 +4 +3 +2 +1

☐ **A** = ☐ **E**

☐ **B** = ☐ **C**

☐ **C** = ☐ **A**

☐ **D** = ☐ **B**

☐ **E** = ☐ **B**

4 Plug **areas** (step 2) into **equations** (step 3). Show that each equality holds.

First study this sample problem:

If your equations don't agree, find out why.

Example: Say you found that **G = 8** sq units, and **H = 12** sq units (step 2), while **3G = 2H** (step 3).

$$3G = 2H$$
$$3 \times 8 = 2 \times 12$$
$$24 = 24$$

Compare **C** and **A:**

Compare **A** and **E:**

Compare **D** and **B:**

Compare **B** and **C:**

Compare **E** and **B:**

Copyright © 2004 by TOPS Learning Systems, Canby OR 97013. Reproduction limited to personal classroom use.

TOPS LEARNING SYSTEMS

Objective

To discover that weight and area increase and decrease proportionally in materials of uniform thickness.

Lesson Notes

2. Require students to write *"units"* and *"sq units"* in their answers. Numbers without units could represent quantities of anything, teabags, giraffes, spare tires, or careless mathematicians. Some students may want to know what a "unit" is. Tell them it's an invented measurement that allows the squares and rectangles to fill the page. (If we used a smaller or larger sheet of paper, these ruler "units," and our squares and rectangles, would shrink or expand in direct proportion.)

3. Accuracy is critical in this step. Students who have carefully centered their balances before using them will be able to differentiate between combinations that truly balance dead level, and others that almost balance. If kids make errors in this step, they won't be able to reconcile the weight proportions with the area proportions of step 2.

4. These calculations show that the area of each square or rectangle is proportional to its weight. This is true for any material of uniform thickness and density.

Don't provide assistance too quickly. Part of scientific literacy is learning to backtrack and isolate errors. Step in only if frustration begins to sour enthusiasm and curiosity. Give your more capable students a chance to succeed on their own, and applaud them when they do.

The sample problem in step 4 uses *imaginary* rectangles G and H to set a pattern that even pre-algebra students can follow. Where you see a letter, plug in the area of the rectangle identified by that letter. Then do the multiplication. See how the equality always holds (ends in an identity).

Answers

2. **A**: 6 units x 6 units = 36 square units
   B: 9 units x 8 units = 72 square units
   C: 12 units x 9 units = 108 square units
   D: 12 units x 12 units = 144 square units
   E: 15 units x 12 units = 180 square units

3.
   5 A = 1 E
   3 B = 2 C
   1 C = 3 A
   1 D = 2 B
   2 E = 5 B

4.

	1C = 3A 1 x 108 = 3 x 36 108 = 108
5A = 1E 5 x 36 = 1 x 180 180 = 180	1D = 2B 1 x 144 = 2 x 72 144 = 144
3B = 2C 3 x 72 = 2 x 108 216 = 216	2E = 5B 2 x 180 = 5 x 72 360 = 360

Extension

Cut out rectangles of notebook paper that have different dimensions but equal areas. Confirm that they have the same weight.

Materials

☐ A paper beam balance.
☐ A pair of scissors.
☐ A calculator (optional).

EDUCATED GUESS

1 Start with 2 sheets of paper that are the same size and weight.

2 Ask a friend to hide paper clips in one of the papers while you look away.

Use a number between 1 and 10.

3 Use your balance to figure out how many paper clips are wrapped inside.

MY GUESS: *ACTUAL COUNT:*

4 Repeat this experiment until you guess the right amount at least 3 times in a row. Tell how you did it.

5 As a bank teller, your job is to count pennies to wrap in 50 ¢ rolls

Tell how you would use a balance to make your job easier.

Copyright © 2004 by TOPS Learning Systems, Canby OR 97013. Reproduction limited to personal classroom use.

TOPS LEARNING SYSTEMS

Objective

To "count" an unknown quantity of paper clips by comparing their weight to a known number of paper clips on a balance.

Lesson Notes

3. Some students may forget to add a sheet of paper to counterbalance the one wrapping the clips. They will predict a number of clips that is too large.

The best way to guess the number of clips is to add them to the pan one at a time until the beam balances. Some students will likely follow a different "hit-or-miss" strategy, wrapping up the number of clips they think is correct, then adding them all at once to the balance. While less efficient, this method should eventually lead to a correct guess.

4. This hide and guess game is popular with younger students. Some may eagerly repeat the procedure for as long as time allows.

5. Post-1982 pennies weigh almost 2 paper clips less than older pennies (see explanation in **Extension B** of activity 15). This count-by-weighing technique works only with pennies of uniform weight, either older or newer than 1982, but not mixed.

An alternate way is to count pennies is to form stacks of equal height. This method takes advantage of uniform thickness.

Answers

3. *Remind students that it's fun to guess correctly, but they shouldn't change their answers if they guessed wrong. This activity lasts for minutes, but integrity and honesty are needed for a lifetime. The next step allows them to refine their guesswork until they achieve correct answers each time.*

4. Center your balance. Place the wrapped-up clips in one pan, and the matching sheet of paper (folded up) in the other pan. Add clips to the lighter side until the beam balances level. The number of clips you add equals the number wrapped in paper.

5. *A lower level answer might simply describe a process similar to counting paper clips:* Center the balance and place 50 pennies in one of the pans. To "count" pennies in groups of 50, simply add them to the other pan until the beam balances level. *(In actuality, this paper balance is not strong enough to hold 50 pennies.)*

A higher level answer might include math:

1 new penny = 6.3 p.c. (activity 15, step 5)
50 pennies = 315 p.c.
1 paper clip = 0.4 grams (activity 15, ext. D)
315 p.c. x 0.4 grams / 1 p.c. = 126 grams

Add pennies to a centered balance that has 315 p.c. (or 126 grams) in one pan. It will balance again when 50 pennies are added to the other side.

Extension

Weigh 0, 1, 2 and 3 *new pennies* in *paper clips*. Graph your data. Extrapolate (extend) your graph line.

Materials

☐ A paper beam balance.
☐ Sheets of paper of equal weight.
☐ Paper clips of uniform size and weight.

MOUNTAIN OF PAPER CLIPS

1 Punch pinholes through all 7 crossmarks along your beam. It's easy if you lay the beam on a pin cushion.

Protect your finger with tape.

Take off both weighing pans.

FOAM CUP

2 Bend the clip on the left end into a hook, and slide a regular clip onto the right end. Adjust so your beam balances level on the **center** pivot.

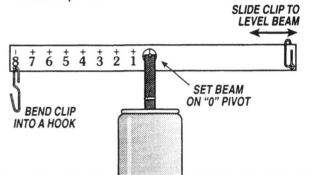

SLIDE CLIP TO LEVEL BEAM

SET BEAM ON "0" PIVOT

BEND CLIP INTO A HOOK

3 Fill in the date table: Find the number of clips that balance the beam when you set it at **each new pivot** position. Then graph your results with a smooth curve.

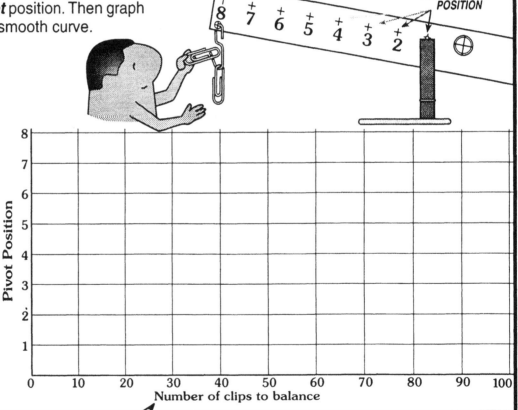

BALANCE LEVEL AT EACH PIVOT POSITION

DATA TABLE

Number of clips to balance	Pivot Position
0	**0**
	1
	2
	3
	4
	5
	6
	7
	8

Pivot Position (y-axis: 1–8)
Number of clips to balance (x-axis: 0–100)

4 Could a "mountain" of paper clips hanging **directly under** pivot #8 raise the beam to a level position? Your graph is telling you the answer.

Copyright © 2004 by TOPS Learning Systems, Canby OR 97013. Reproduction limited to personal classroom use.

TOPS LEARNING SYSTEMS

Objective

To graph how the force required to balance an off-center beam increases as it is applied closer to the pivot.

Introduction/Background

When plotting points on their graphs, inexperienced students may need some coaching. Show them how to circle their points to "protect" their data. Then, when they connect the points, the line should stop at each circle and resume on the opposite side. Otherwise the data points will simply disappear into the graph line.

Drawing a smooth curve is difficult for many kids. Suggest they sketch **very lightly** where they think the line might be placed, then evaluate the results. Some points might fall to either side of a good curve. If the line wobbles up and down or turns any "corners," students have tried too hard to target every point instead of averaging them into a smooth sweep.

To locate the "number of clips to balance" on the horizontal x-axis, kids need to know how to estimate between 1 and 10 on the number line. This review may help:

Locate these numbers on the number line:

5, 7, 2+, 15-, 11, 18

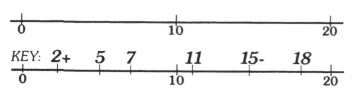

Lesson Notes

3. A whole number of paper clips will not always balance the beam at each position, so a plus or minus can be used to indicate when slightly more or less weight is required. Enterprising students can get a more precise number by using their Paper Clip Strip weights from activity 15.

At pivot position 7, the paper clip hook may not be large enough to hold all the required clips (69 in our test). Further, the cluster of clips may eventually touch the support, which will make accurate balancing impossible.

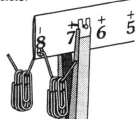

These problems are solved by bending a clip as shown below to make a double hook. This "w" shape will hold more clips, and suspend them closer to the beam. Your students may discover other engineering solutions, as well.

4. This abstract question can become a concrete experience. Punch a pinhole on the line above position 8. Suspend the pin with paper clips or string as shown. Students will find that **no** amount of downward force on that line can raise the beam to a level position.

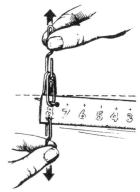

It's interesting to note that if you shift the pivot very slightly to the right, perhaps to "position 7.9" or so, you can pull the beam up to level with relative ease.

Materials

☐ A math balance.

☐ Paper clips of uniform size and weight. Since this activity requires 75 or more (depending on the weight of your paper clips and your beam), you may want to organize your class into a smaller number of research groups.

☐ A straight pin and tape.

☐ A styrofoam cup or other "pincushion."

Answers

3. Answers may vary with the weight of your paper clips. But graph curves should look much like this:

# of clips	Pivot position
0	0
1+	1
3+	2
6	3
10	4
17	5
31	6
69	7

*Looks like we have a classic case of **asymptote**!*

4. *(Students should extend the curved graph line all the way to the right border to answer this question.)* As the graph line approaches pivot position 8, it runs ever more nearly parallel to it, and looks like it might never cross it. So, even an infinite number of paper clips is not heavy enough to raise the beam to a level position.

SUPPLEMENTARY
CUTOUT

SQUARES and RECTANGLES

Copyright © 2004 by TOPS Learning Systems, Canby OR 97013

Feedback!

Dear Educator and Student,

Please write us! We are motivated by feedback from our public. Praise or criticism? Bring it on! Did you find an error? Can you suggest ways to improve this program? We really want to hear about it.

You'd like information about our other publications? We'll happily send you our latest free catalog. Or visit **www.topscience.org**. It's spilling over with free sample lessons and helpful information.

For whatever reason, we'd love to hear from you, and will carefully consider your input. Email us at **tops@canby.com**, or post this convenient self-mailer.

Sincerely,

Ron & Peg

Ron and Peg Marson
author and illustrator

module title _____ date _____

name _____

address _____

city _____ state _____ zip_____

1st FOLD   TAPE CLOSED

2nd FOLD

_____

_____

_____

PLEASE
STAMP

TOPS Learning Systems
342 S Plumas Street
Willows, CA 95988

Made in the
USA
Middletown, DE

75222953R00038